AND etc.,
aps of Portsmouth no.3a)
ld.MS.16371a. 19.8 × 38.8 in.
ritish Library Board

THE
NAVAL
ARCHITECT

Pachelle inc.
(Incorporated Since 1981)

THE
NAVAL
ARCHITECT

David J. Doust

First published by Pachelle Inc., 1999 and printed and bound by Transcontinental Printing Inc. - Métrolitho division, Sherbrooke.

Pachelle Inc. (1981)
P.O. 381
Ayer's Cliff, QC J0B 1C0
CANADA
(819) 838-5049 / 5070
www.oceanwide.com/pachelle

Page layout: Susan J. Fletcher, C.R.I.N.A.
Printed and bound in Canada

Canadian Cataloguing in Publication Data
Doust, David J. (David John), 1925-
The Naval Architect
Includes bibliographical references and index.
ISBN 0-9681858-1-9

1. Doust, David J. (David John), 1925. 2. Naval Architects
Canada Biography I. Title. II. Pachelle Inc.
VM140.D68A3 1999   623.8'1'092   C99-901388-2
Includes: Nomenclature

INTRODUCTION

The Naval Architect is a graphic account of the author's experiences over a 60 year period, starting as a young apprentice at H.M. Dockyard, Portsmouth, England during World War 2. The book describes in detail the many roles which naval architects can play in marine research and development, including ship design and construction, marine consulting, ship financial analysis, and as expert witness in the courts, and the arbitration and mediation processes.

The first 20 years of that period included many phases of marine research conducted at the Ship Division of the National Physical Laboratory, (N.P.L.), Teddington, England, where the author worked as a hydrodynamicist. Experiments conducted in that period at the N.P.L., for Clients worldwide, included those for vessels of all types such as passenger and cargo ships, ferries, tugs and barges, tankers, bulk carriers, oceanographic research vessels, RO/RO ships, Lakers, Light ships, and many others.

Specific research at the N.P.L. also conducted by the author, included experiments on sideways launching, yacht research, flow visualisation tests, and the berthing and docking of large ships. Some prevailing attitudes towards ship research in the U.K. at that time are then discussed, leading up to the demolition of these ship research facilities at the N.P.L., and it is suggested that their eventual demise was inevitable.

The author's experiences then follow on to Montreal, Canada to which country he emigrated in 1966. He describes marine developments in Canada and several other countries in which he worked as a marine consultant, on behalf of commercial and governmental agencies, particularly in the fisheries sector.

Materials uses in marine construction, and practical applications leading up to their latest technological development, are described in detail Ship financing and marine insurance for joint ventures in developing countries are discussed, together with some lessons which still need to be learned by those participating in such ventures Some typical examples of results derived from techno-economic analyses of vessel performance, are also presented by the author in easily understood graphical format.

Drawing on his wide experience as an expert witness, the author then shows that there are several other aspects of marine litigation, in which naval architects can and should take a useful role. In addition to the courts, he discusses the arbitration and mediation processes as alternative methods of dispute resolution, in which independent technical and scientific expertise is often required, but not always available. New trends in ship design and construction to meet the new challenges ahead are finally suggested, which will affect port developments, shipping operations, ship project management, life-saving requirements, environmental safety, and navigation in ice infested waters

The author wishes to thank all those who assisted him in the production of this manuscript. Susan J. Fletcher, Partner and the original founder of Pachelle (1981) Inc. who did most of the archival research and assembly of the records and photographs which had been accumulated over the years. To Alice E. Doust, B.A.(Hons), his lifetime friend, who proof read the original work in its early stages of development, to Geoff. Hayes, a fellow author from the old days at N.P.L., who made many valuable suggestions for improvements in the original manuscript, and to Captain Ray Espley, Stikeman Elliott, Montreal, who made several valuable comments on the navigational aspects of the book. The author also wishes to especially thank the Royal Institution of Naval Architects, London, England, and his benefactor, who awarded him the Martell Scholarship in 1945 and which thus launched him on his career as a naval architect.

PREFACE

In the beginning...

D.—208. (Revised—October, 1917.)

This Indenture made the 19th day of August 19 40.

_{* The Apprentice.} between*

       David John DOUST

                  (being of the age of   fifteen   years)
hereinafter called " the Apprentice " of the first part,

       John Edward DOUST

       of   47 Park Road,
                  Gosport.

_{† Father, Guardian, or next Friend.}   (the†   Father   of the said

_{‡ Principal Officer of the Dockyard, to be described by his Name and Office.}   David John DOUST   ), of the second part, and‡

       Christopher Wortley KERRIDGE Esq., R.C.N.C.,
       Manager, Constructive Department,
             H.M. Dockyard,
              Portsmouth.

who with his successors in his said office or other the person appointed from time to time to perform the duties of his said office, is hereinafter called " the Master " (for and on behalf of the King's most Excellent Majesty, His Heirs and Successors), of the third part, WITNESSETH that in consideration of the covenants and agreements of the Master hereinafter contained, the Apprentice (with the consent and approbation of the said party of the second part, testified by his being a party hereto), Doth by these presents, freely and voluntarily put and place himself Apprentice to the Master to learn and exercise the art or occupation of

       Fitter   in the several branches or departments thereof in which Apprentices are, or shall or may be employed in His Majesty's Dockyard at   Portsmouth   , or other Home Yard, or other places, as may at any time or times during the term of his Apprenticeship, be directed by the Commissioners for executing the Office of Lord High Admiral of the United Kingdom of Great Britain and Ireland, to serve as an Apprentice with and under the Master for the use and benefit of His said Majesty, His Heirs and Successors, for, and during and unto the end of the full term of five years to be computed from the day of the date of entry on the Yard books.

C.N.² 2363/06.
Sta. 268/17.
Sta. 80/23.

(1728) Wt. 18584/D5495 3m 7/39 S.E.R. Ltd. Gp. 671.

And the Apprentice and the party of the second part do severally
hereby covenant with the Master that he the said Apprentice shall and
will during the said term faithfully and industriously serve the Master,
and also such persons as he the said Apprentice may be placed under by
the Master, and obey all their respective lawful commands, orders, and
directions, and will observe all rules and regulations which are or shall be
from time to time made by the said Commissioners in respect, of
Apprentices, and generally will diligently conduct himself, and use his best
abilities and endeavours towards his improvement and perfection in the said
art or occupation of   Fitter   , and for the good and benefit
of His said Majesty, His Heirs and Successors therein. And also that
he the said Apprentice shall not and will not at any time during the said
term do, or willingly suffer to be done, any act or thing whatsoever whereby
the goods and effects of His said Majesty, His Heirs and Successors, can,
shall, or may in anywise be embezzled, injured, or damaged, or His officers
or service defrauded, or otherwise prejudiced in any manner howsoever,
nor shall, nor will, at any time absent himself from the service or work
without the leave of the Master or any Officers under whose authority he
may be placed; nor contract marriage during the period of this Indenture;
nor be guilty by word or action of any immoral, indecent, irregular, or im-
proper conduct or behaviour in any respect whatsoever, but shall and will
demean himself at all times with strict propriety and submission to his
superiors.

And the party of the second part doth hereby covenant with the Master
that he, the said party of the second part, can and will from time to time
during the said term find and provide for the Apprentice good and sufficient
board, lodging, clothing, and washing, and all other necessaries proper for
his personal accommodation and benefit suitable to his said intended
situation. And also provide such implements, working tools, and
instruments as the customs of the trade require to enable him to learn and
practice the said art or occupation of   Fitter

And in consideration of all and singular the premises the Master doth
hereby (for and on behalf of His said Majesty, His Heirs and Successors)
covenant with the Apprentice and the party of the second part, and each of
them, that he the said Apprentice duly observing, performing, and keeping
all the covenants and agreements on his part herein-before contained shall
be properly taught and fully instructed in the said art or occupation of
      Fitter   And shall during such time as he shall continue
at his work be entitled to and receive all the wages, emoluments, and advantages which the said Commissioners shall from time to time think
proper to allow to Apprentices of his description.

And lastly, it is hereby especially stipulated and agreed by and
between the said parties hereto, that in case the said Apprentice shall for
the space of one week during the said term (unless disabled from work by
sickness), absent himself from his service and employment under this
Indenture, without the license and consent of the Master or other person
authorised in that behalf, or shall neglect to perform the reasonable and

3

necessary work required from him, or shall be guilty of embezzlement or
other criminal conduct, or shall for a period of six consecutive calendar
months be disabled from work by sickness, or shall suffer from any disease
or complaint that would render his continued employment dangerous to
himself or his fellow employés, it shall be lawful for the Master to declare
this Indenture to be void by notice in writing, signed by the Master, and
left at the usual or last place of abode of the party of the second part, or
if he be dead, or cannot be found, by exhibiting the said notice publicly in
the Office of the Cashier, and also in front of the Muster Offices of the
said Yard, and thereupon this Indenture shall be void accordingly.

In witness whereof the parties to these Presents have hereunto sub-
scribed their names and affixed their seals the day and year first above
written.

*Signed, Sealed, and Delivered by
all the Parties (being first duly
stamped) in the presence of*

....Witness.
DEPARTMENTAL HIGHER CLERICAL OFFICER.

David John Doust

John Edward Doust

Christopher Worthy Kemdy

TABLE OF CONTENTS

APPENDIX

INDEX

ACKNOWLEDGMENTS

Susan J. Fletcher, C.R.I.N.A., Partner and the original founder of Pachelle (1981) Inc. who encouraged me to continue with my series following *The Expert Witness*, 1997, who did most of the archival research and assembly of the records and photographs which had been accumulated over the years.

Alice E. Doust, B.A. (Hons.), his lifetime friend, who proof read the original work in its early stages of development.

Mr. Geoff Hayes, a fellow author from the old days at N.P.L., who made many valuable suggestions for improvements in the original manuscript.

Captain Ray Esday, R.D.M.R.I.N. Stikeman Elliott, Montreal who made several valuable comments on the navigational aspects of the book.

Kelly Fletcher, B.B.A. and Matthew Meanchoff, B.A. then students who shared and contributed their ideas in the formulative stages of both *The Expert Witness* and *The Naval Architect* to benefit the non technical readership.

The author wishes to especially thank the Royal Institution of Naval Architects, London, England, and his benefactor, who awarded him the Martell Scholarship in 1945 and which thus launched him on his career as a naval architect.

The British Library, London, U.K.
The Aluminum Association, Washington, D.C.
The Society of Naval Architects and Marine Engineers, New York City, U.S.A.
The MacGregor Group (MacGregor News), South Devon, U.K.
Hanjin Heavy Industries
Mr. A.C. Hardy, B.Sc., member S.N.A.M.E.
Bender Shipyards, Mobile, Alabama, U.S.A.

-TO MY BENEFACTOR MARTELL-

CHAPTER I

THE EARLY YEARS IN PORTSMOUTH AND GOSPORT

I have found many people puzzled by the term "naval architect". They do not seem to relate readily to what a naval architect actually does, and this is not altogether surprising, since we as a profession are so diversified in our various roles in the marine industry at large. Perhaps in the last century, and before, when ships were made of wood and often conceived by only one designer, it was much easier to understand that "naval architect" could be equated to "ship designer". Even in the early part of this century, one man could claim, without much fear of contradiction, that he had designed the TITANIC.! Nowadays, ships are much more complex and generally the product of a design team, either based in a shipyard, or working as a firm of naval architects and marine consultants.

I was fortunate indeed to know that I wanted to be a naval architect at the tender age of ten, born and bred as I was in the famous naval port of Portsmouth, Hampshire, England. At a recent family reunion in Gosport, just over the ferry from Portsmouth, I again got a great thrill seeing the bustling harbour, full of navy ships of all kinds, and the ferries, cruise ships, tugs and other smaller craft, which seem to abound at all times of the day, and night. It reminded me again of how busy the harbour had been in my youth, and my aspirations to be part of all that marine activity. Some young people today seem to have a lot of difficulty in knowing what they want to be when they grow up.

Perhaps there is "something" in the genes which helps some, but not others, to gravitate into certain chosen professions. Musicians, for example, seem to beget musicians, artists generally seem to nurture their youngsters into similar careers, and many other professions, trades and industries seem to encourage sons and daughters to follow on in the family traditions of their forebears. I was lucky enough to come from a navy background. My father, his father, and his father before him, all had naval careers, whilst my mother's family had similar marine connections. My mentor and uncle, Captain William Alexander (Sandy) Doust, was the famous marine salvor in World War 2 who pioneered certain kinds of salvage operations, was himself an author, and has been cited in several publications, notably "Mud, Muscle and Miracles" - Marine Salvage in the United States Navy, by Captain C.A. Bartholomew, U.S.N., Department of the Navy, Washington, D.C. (see Refs.1, 2). He helped me a lot to get started in my early career. I was 14 years of age when World War 2 started in September, 1939. That year I had worked through my summer holidays, helping to make "Carley floats", prior to starting work at H.M. Dockyard, Portsmouth, where I had won entry to a 5 year apprenticeship, through an open competition. Carley floats helped to save the lives of many thousands of gallant seamen who were torpedoed during the war, as they were unsinkable and designed as life rafts, complete with rope hand holds, which required to be spliced with a marlin spike. Since my summer job was to do the splicing, and the ropes were very oily and rough, my hands at the age of 14 were really quite tough. It certainly helped me at catching the ball at cricket, at least!

Those early years of the war were almost without incident, except in Scotland, where the Germans managed to kill that famous rabbit, which became the theme of the song, "Run rabbit, run rabbit, run-run-run."! In Portsmouth and Gosport we were not so fortunate, once the Allied evacuation from Dunkirk began. I can still recall going to work, over on the ferry, from Gosport to Portsmouth early one morning and seeing a group of Heinkels dive bombing the harbour station, and the trains falling through into the sea. We had a ringside seat from the ferry boat. One of our anti-aircraft guns, by a minor miracle, managed to bring one of the planes down. They were usually much more proficient in knocking holes in peoples' roofs! I saw one of the machine gunners on a foreign merchant ship in the harbour, shoot at the pilot of the dive bomber, as he floated gently down by parachute. I saw him stiffen, as the bullets ripped into his body, on the way down, I remember thinking even then, just how much hate had been generated by the war, how the Luftewaffe had done the same thing in Warsaw and other cities in Europe, against defenceless civilian populations. There were numerous other home events in the early part of the war, with swarms of enemy bombers and fighters overhead, only the occasional Spitfire or Hurricane to fend them off, and the usual array of "barrage" ballons, which seemed only to serve as target practice. They often ended up going down, in flames, but the thinking at the time seemed to be that they somehow served as deterrents, perhaps more psychological than real. There was another memorable occasion when some Junker dive bombers had a field day at the Gosport aerodrome, near Military Road. I saw the bomb doors open as they came over our house, the bombs released, and the havoc they caused to the hangars and planes on the base camp. I also vividly remembered the Graff Zeppelin which flew over almost the same spot, not long before the war, with the military photographers taking aerial shots from the observation platform underneath.

I was an assistant air raid warden as soon as I was old enough to be one, and was kitted out with a steel helmet, a working gas mask, gloves and other gear which went with the job. Every night was the same, a lone enemy heavy bomber overhead, droning away for hours on end, until it was time to drop its bomb and return back to base in France, only to be replaced very shortly with another of the same. These tactics were very wearing on the nerves of the mainly women, children, and elderly, who made up the majority of the civilian population at that time. All men over 18 years of age were conscripted for the armed forces, and mainly absent overseas, except for those who were in some exempted category, or working in industries which were categorised as a wartime occupation. We lived in Park Road, Gosport at that early time of the war, right near to Haslar Creek. I was back there on a memory trip recently, and was amazed to see the changes in the last 50 to 60 years. What had been a winding open road, running alongside the muddy creek, is now fully paved, bordered by a fine brick and stone wall, and luxury houses and apartments. One night, when the lone bomber was droning away overhead, as usual, I was on patrol with the senior warden, quite near the bridge which crosses the creek. We fell to the ground, as we heard the piercing scream of the bomb as it hit, right on the edge of the road, most of it falling in the muddy creek. We were both sprayed with mud, gravel, and small debris from the blast, but apart from some minor cuts and bruises we were very lucky to be alive. I remember arriving home shortly afterwards. My mother fainted when she saw the blood on my face and chest. Not long after that, we were subjected to probably one of the nastiest anti-personnel devices ever rained down on a civilian population, the "Molotov" cocktail. These were explosive devices, implanted in the magnesium flares which were routinely being dropped in large numbers on Gosport and Portsmouth, during the nightly air raids. As air raid wardens, we had often removed magnesium flares from the upstair rooms of houses, whose roofs had been penetrated by them. Once the Molotov cocktails appeared on the scene, however, it became far too hazardous to do so. There were many terrible burns inflicted on fire fighters in action, before the real horror of these devices became more widely known. As my birthday is in early May, it so happened that the age conditions for entry into the H.M. Dockyard scheme, permitted me to take the apprenticeship examinations at the earliest possible time, despite the War! Some other boys, still within a permissible two-year entry period, were almost two years older than I, and in the same class! This two year age difference, at that time of life, imposed quite a heavy learning handicap, as the Admiralty training program was very competitive, so that although we all received the same *practical* training, it was designed to cut the numbers of students proceeding to the next year of theoretical studies, by about 50%, each year.

The result was that in the Upper Dockyard School, in which I had qualified to commence studies in 1939, 120 boys of the first year, were automatically cut to 60 to commence the second year, cut to 30 to commence the third year, and cut to 20 to commence the fourth and final year. Boys who were excluded from proceeding from one year to the next, continued their studies in the Lower School at the appropriate levels. Despite this two year age handicap, I survived into the final and fourth year of studies, won a Whitworth prize, and then went on to The Admiralty Experiment Works at Haslar, Gosport, to finish my apprenticeship. This proved to be a most stimulating experience, as I was put to work, for one year, with a select team of scientists co-opted from various universities, who were working to solve the sinking of ships, caused by the German-made, acoustic mines. These were dropped by parachute into the estuaries of large rivers and harbours around the coast of Britain, during the war, and caused havoc to all forms of shipping at the time. The Haslar team solved the mystery, discovered how the mines worked and were activated. The result was that small tugs could be used to tow expendable pontoons, or similar vessels, ahead of the larger ships, detonate the mines and make the passage way safe for naval ships coming up from behind. In 1945, whilst still working at A.E.W. Haslar, I then took that year's open examinations for the Royal, Whitworth and Martell Scholarships, in competition with boys of my own age group, and won all three scholarships. The Martell Scholarship is awarded by the Royal Institution of Naval Architects, London, every three years, so that my timing to train as a naval architect could not have been better. I remember thinking, however, that I really must have wanted to be a naval architect as the annual value of the Martell was only 150 sterling, compared with the corresponding values of 400 sterling for the others, but these would have led automatically to a different career in engineering.

Anyhow, I accepted the Martell, with many thanks to my benefactor, and tried to manage on the much lower income. The R.I.N.A. took pity on me after one year, and increased my annual income to 200 sterling, which was just about enough to live on in those times!

CHAPTER II

UP NORTH, AND DOWN SOUTH AT N.P.L.

I then elected to study at King's College, then part of Durham University, but located at Newcastle on Tyne (now the University of Newcastle on Tyne), under the tutilage of Professor L.C. Burrill, a leading propeller designer at that time. My previous theoretical training and experience at Portsmouth Dockyard qualified me for exemption from the first year of studies at King's College, so that I was able to proceed directly into the second year of a three year degree course in naval architecture. In 1947 I graduated B.Sc., with distinction, and then proceeded, in the final year of my scholarship, to take an Honours degree. In 1948, I graduated B.Sc.,with first class honours, and received the R. L. Weighton Memorial Gold Medal. It was rather sad that my father, who had died prematurely the year before, could not be there to see me graduate or to advise me on the next most important step after graduation, that is what job to take. I did, however, receive a handsome offer to work as a scientific officer at the National Physical Laboratory, Teddington, Middlesex, which I accepted, and which formed the basis of my first career as a hydrodynamicist. I worked in the Ship Division of that laboratory for over 18 years, and was mainly responsible for the design and testing of all vessels under 250 feet in length. These included fishing vessels of all kinds, tugs, tug and barge systems, light vessels, yachts, and many other special projects which required evaluation in both smooth and rough water. It was also part of the work to perform and plan trials for all new ships which had been tested in the Ship

7

The Naval Architect

Division, usually in collaboration with the British Ship Research Association, with whom we enjoyed a close working relationship. This excellent scheme enabled designers, such as we, to compare model test results in calm water and in waves, with actual full scale ship performance at sea. Fishing vessels are unique in that they are about the only type of ship which are actually *expected* to work at sea in storm conditions, when other much larger ships are hove-to. Since fishing vessels were my designated responsibility at the N.P.L. for many years, it was therefore a unique opportunity, not given to many, to learn about some of the effects of the sea on ship motions, ship manoeuvrability, and speed, in relation to their shape. I attended the sea trials of most of Britain's deep sea trawler fleet for at least ten years. Most of them passed my scrutiny at the N.P.L., and after rigorous testing and modifications, many became top earners in various fishing companies based in Hull, Grimsby, Fleetwood and other famous fishing ports. It almost became routine that the winner of the Silver Cod Trophy in any one year, had been tested at the N.P.L. Even some French Owners, and others, insisted on having their ships tested by me at the N.P.L. in that period, and stated so in writing when I left for another career in Canada, just prior to which I was awarded the degree of Dr. Technicae, by the University of Norway for my work on computer-aided ship design Later in my career at the N.P.L., I was also fortunate to be nominated, I think by default of my colleagues!, as the recipient of the Duke of Edinburgh's scheme. This scheme enabled me to make two crossings of the Atlantic in the severe storm conditions, of Beaufort 12. One was over to Canada on the passenger ship "Empress of Britain", and the return trip was from Halifax, Nova Scotia, on the grain ship "Beaverlake", each trip encountering up to 60 foot waves and high winds. I will never forget the helpless feeling of being so insignificant, in relation to the forces of the sea and wind. The trip back to Antwerp took 14 days, instead of the more usual 10 days, and most of that was spent in rolling about 30 degrees from side to side, except when the grain boards shifted! This induced, at least, an additional 5 degree list which set my hand calculator to work, as I estimated the likely effects of a further shift of cargo! Fortunately it was not then my time to go, but I did hear a rumour that she did finally sink in rather similar circumstances. I do know that when we finally berthed in Antwerp, I was definitely walking with a distinct rolling motion, which was not entirely symmetrical. On some of the earlier North Sea trials, when the weather had changed suddenly for the very worst, I recall the "wall" of water all around us as we sank into the wave troughs, and then suddenly looking around at a range of what seemed to be mountain peaks of water, as we shot up on the top of those waves. I used to pray that the welders and riveters of those newly-built ships had really done their job, especially when on one occasion part of the bridge front was set back *nearly a foot*, due to the force of the waves coming over the bow.

In complete contrast, I remember being with a trials party, taking the research vessel, "Sir William Hardy", the first diesel electric ship of its kind, from Aberdeen, round the top of Scotland via the Pentland Firth, across to Cape Wrath, and thence down the west coast of Scotland to the port of Glasgow. We were looking for bad weather, and specially chose the time of year when storms can be expected in that region. The ship was instrumented to the hilt, with all manner of pitch, roll and heel recorders, accelerometers, stress meters, automatic, self-recording, wind speed and direction anemometers, and all the required engine room apparatus needed to record the engine torque, propeller revolutions and shaft output in bad weather. In view of the advice I had received from several well-meaning Scots, I was dressed in a recently acquired suit of Harris tweed. I believe that most instruments during the entire trip read zero, or recorded no worthwhile data, since by a freak of fortune, we enjoyed the most wonderful week of calm weather imaginable, with temperatures in the eighties Fahrenheit. I recall sitting on deck, baking hot, with my trousers turned up for comfort, and attempting to achieve a sun tan at the very least.

Our Superintendent at the time was Dr. James Foggo Allan, formerly of the Sir William Denny Tank at Dumbarton, who was definitely not amused on our team's return to the N.P.L. to discuss the trial results, which were of course of little value for our purposes in gathering ship data in bad weather.

CHAPTER III

LIFE AT N.P.L.

My eighteen years at the Ship Division of the National Physical Laboratory, Teddington, Middlesex, England were very memorable and happy ones. I lived with my family nearby at Hampton on Thames, and used to walk through that still delightful Bushy Park every day, on my way to the laboratory which is not far from Hampton Court palace. I particularly enjoyed the daily company of fellow scientists, many working in other disciplines, and over lunch would be able to chat about such topics as the " D.N.A. double spiral helix" and its probable composite structure, the early development of the N.P.L. computer, with its enormous diodes, the aerodynamic flow over ship superstructures, especially the flow of gases from ship's funnels, the latest ideas on multi-dimensional statistical theory and its application to experimental modelling, the analysis of metallic structural failure, the uses of ciné photography in model experimentation and many other physical aspects of their work. I soon found out that "physical" as in National "Physical" Laboratory, covered many diverse subjects, some of which could be applied to my own discipline of hydrodynamics.

Because of my close association with the fishing industry at that time, for example, I became involved in the method of "sideways launching" of ships. It is not so well known that sideways launching of ships is much more widely practised, worldwide, than generally thought to be the case. "End-on" launching of ships is more common for larger ships with unrestricted widths of water, although when the shipyard is

SIDE LAUNCHING OF SHIPS – WITH SPECIAL REFERENCE TO TRAWLERS

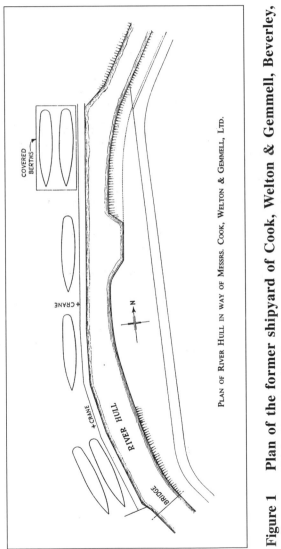

Figure 1   Plan of the former shipyard of Cook, Welton & Gemmell, Beverley, Yorkshire, England.

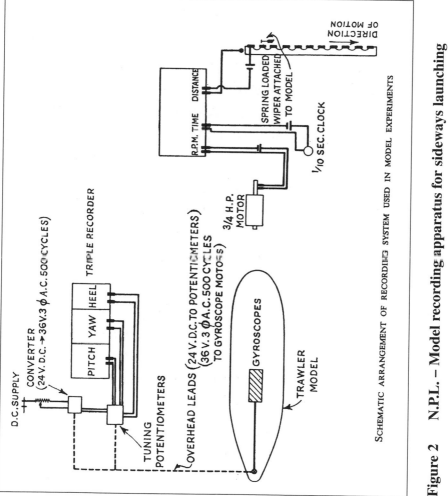

Figure 2   N.P.L. – Model recording apparatus for sideways launching

located on a river or where the width available to launch is restricted, sideways launching is the one which offers the simplest solution, since the vessel can be brought to rest after launching, well within twice the beam of the ship. This is obviously much less than the length of the ship, which often exceeds the width of the available launching site, severely restricting the sizes of ships which can be launched by the "end-on" method. Many yards, all over the world, therefore use the sideways launching method.(see Refs. 3, 4, 5) Figure 1 shows the plan of the former shipyard of Cook, Welton and Gemmell, Beverley, Yorkshire, U.K., where many of the finest deep sea trawlers were built in the period from 1948 to 1966, and beyond. In 1953, we were approached by the Managing Director, Ambrose Hunter, a well known shipbuilder and fine gentleman of that era in British shipbuilding, to see if we could determine the parameters which govern sideways launching, and in particular, whether we could provide any guidelines on the maximum sizes of vessels which could be safely launched at his yard. I was designated to examine the problem, and organised a team to record a typical full scale launch of a large side trawler at the Beverley yard. This entailed organising a test procedure to measure the speed of the vessel during the launch, its roll, pitch and yaw throughout the event from the time of release to the final position of rest in the river, the impact pressures on the hull surface during its impact with the water, the stability of the vessel during the launch, and complete ciné records of the event. I co-opted the assistance of our N.P.L. Photographic Unit, headed by my friend and colleague, Charles Guthrie, who gave us his enthusiastic support for the project. We devised a procedure, whereby the vessel could be observed photographically, as it made its critical outward and inward rolls at the end of the launching ways, as well as general views of the vessel as it travelled down the ways and

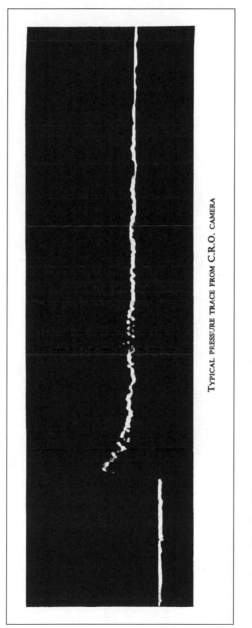

TYPICAL PRESSURE TRACE FROM C.R.O. CAMERA

Figure 3   Typical Pressure trace from C.R.O. camera.

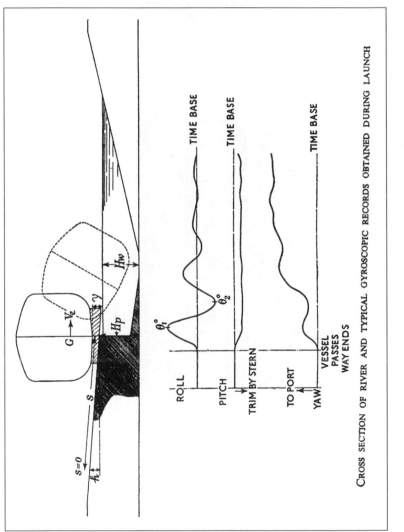

Figure 4 Typical gyroscopic records of side-launched vessel.

during the period when it struck the water.(Fig.4) All readings obtained from the tests were synchronised, so that subsequent analysis could be made of the hull pressures, ship motions, and speeds of travel throughout the launch at any required moment in time. Working in collaboration with the shipyard personnel, we were able to record the launching of a further five vessels, varying in length from 141 to 180 feet in length. After each launch, we also conducted inclining experiments to determine the transverse stability of the vessels, which were later used to correlate the results with simulated test conditions on the model scale. Having examined the sideways problem on the full scale, it was decided to simulate this particular method of launching on the model scale. The launch site at the shipyard was reproduced, to a scale of 1/12, and systematic variations were made in way-end velocity, transverse ship stability, static drop at the end of the ways, the width of the river, the depth of water in the river, the displacement of the vessel at launch, the freeboard, and other physical parameters thought to govern the motion of the vessel. In order to determine if there was any substantial scale effect between the model and full scale results, the model test program commenced with a simulation of the first actual sideways launch recorded at the shipyard. These, and other results, confirmed our previous calculations that there was no significant scale effect difference in the important first outward angle of roll at the way ends, nor on the sometimes dangerous first return roll, towards the edge of the quayside. The outward roll of the vessel is of course critical to its survival, since it can capsize if its centre of gravity is too high, or the static drop at the way ends too great. Again, on the return roll to the quayside, it can sometimes hit the edge of the quay, and cause severe structural damages to both itself and the quay. Fortunately, these initial tests were very positive, so that we could proceed with full confidence,

MODEL ON MAXIMUM OUTWARD ROLL
SHOWING GYROSCOPES

Figure 5   **Typical side-launched model under test at N.P.L.**

both experimentally and theoretically, knowing that the effects of any systematic changes in our model experiments would be reproduced on the full scale. Another very important factor is the impact pressure on the underwater hull form, as the vessel strikes the water. The shipyard management was uncertain as to the limits of pressure to which the hull was subjected on impact, nor of their possible effects on the hull structure. We therefore devised a test procedure to study the effect of hull impact pressures, over a wide range of test conditions. The hull pressures were recorded at nine positions around the midship section, as illustrated in Figure 2. The pressure gauges were made "in-house" in the laboratory workshop, which was noted for its excellent workmanship. The pressure changes at impact and afterwards, were recorded on a cathode ray tube, as shown typically in figure 3. At the time this was considered state of the art technology, and is still about the best way to get reliable results. The maximum pressures around the midship section were found to be up to 16.0 pounds per square inch, or just over one atmosphere. It was therefore suggested that some internal temporary bracing of the hull, in way of any heavy machinery items, would be advisable when the static drop of the vessel exceeds 25% of the water depth at the site. Figure 5 shows a side-launched model under test at N.P.L. In 1956-7, we carried out further more extensive sideways launching experiments at the Ship Division of the N.P.L. Teddington. These covered a much wider range of ship stability and were conducted on much fuller hull forms; coasters and hopper dredgers, both built in relatively large numbers throughout the world (see Ref. 4). These results were specifically aimed at determining the safe limits of water depth, and static drop at the way ends, for a wide range of ship conditions. They showed that as ships decrease in fullness, their launch stability can also be reduced with safety, for otherwise identical conditions. Subsequent

SIDE LAUNCH AT WILMINGTON, CALIFORNIA, 1943
VESSEL 6,000 TONS D.W.

Figure 6   Full scale side launch-6,000 tons DWT vessel.

This photograph is reproduced by kind permission of Mr A.C. Hardy, B.Sc.Member.

events were to show how widely these results are being used and studied around the world, even to this day. (Figure 6)

The foregoing, fundamental, practical approach to marine research was always my guiding light. I was never too much impressed or agreed with the airy-fairy attitude of the so-called, "pure" researchers. They seem to think that whether they produce anything useful, or not, their future is assured. Nothing could be further from the truth, and as many who were invited to retire early have since discovered; the bitter truth is that "research" has a bottom line! This large philosophical difference between pure and applied scientific thinking still abounds today, and was even more prevalent in my time at N.P.L., between 1948 and 1966. As subsequent events were to show, the consequences of such a completely impractical approach to ship research, aided and abetted by a few misguided implants, who came and left N.P.L. in short order, with little or no knowledge of simple economics, were to cost the British taxpayer millions.

In the mid 1950's, Ship Division, N.P.L. was approached by Mr. W. Lochridge who was then working on the concept of "stern trawling", a British invention of fishing over the stern, which eventually became adopted worldwide. The fore-runner of all such trawlers was the "Fairtry", owned by Chr. Salvesen & Co. Ltd., Leith, Scotland. Mr. Lochridge wanted to try out his new ideas by running model tests of the vessel in the towing tank at N.P.L.. The vessel was a single screw, stern trawler, equipped to process the catch immediately it came on board, in the form of freshly frozen fish fillets, fish meal and fish liver oil. The catch envisaged was mainly cod, and some haddock, which then abounded in great quantities North of the British Isles and as far away as Iceland, the Norwegian and Barents Seas, and the White Sea, all of which were fished by large vessels of all types, mainly catching fish over the side in the old traditional way, and stowing their catches on ice. The main problem at that time was the fact that fish stowed on ice has a limited shelf life, about 16 days, after which they start to deteriorate and become unfit for human consumption. As the productive fishing grounds became more remote from the home ports, such as Hull, Grimsby and Lowestoft and Aberdeen, to name but a few, the time spent in going to and from the grounds increased, and the available time spent in fishing therefore decreased. The economics of freezing the catch on board, and thus removing the urgency to return to the home port for auctioning of the fresh catch, became more apparent. The "Fairtry" concept, however, had to rely on a more efficient method of trawling, which could be applied in conjunction with the other essential design requirements of handling the catch, stowing it below deck, and then processing it into a filleted, frozen form. This led naturally to the idea of fishing over the stern. We made a model of the vessel, including the stern ramp, and fitted it with all the envisaged fishing gear, including trawl boards and bobbins to keep the mouth of the net open, stern "gallows" and winches to bring the net on board. It became obvious from these rather idealised tests, that the design of the trawl boards, or "paravanes" was critical to the success of the method, and that keeping the net open at ship speeds of about 3 to 5 knots was the main problem, otherwise the fish would not be able to enter the net. Attention was therefore directed to the best arrangements of trawl boards and their connecting links to the main trawl warps, to achieve a good running attitude of the net, both on the bottom and at mid-depths, which latter method eventually became the favoured method used to catch herring, and similar pelagic species, which live mainly at middle depths of water. It was only some 8 years or more, after the Fairtry came into service, that the British deep-sea trawler fleets started to change to stern trawling. Meanwhile, in Germany, Norway, France, Poland, Canada and several other other countries, the stern fishing method had been developed further, and rapidly became the fishing method of choice. The additional change to freezing the catch on board, followed on logically, as countries extended their fishing zones, and as the catches became more and more scarce, and more remote from the home ports. It is sad indeed, today, to visit some of those once busy East Coast fishing ports around the British Isles, and to see the effects of over-fishing, which has now plagued all major fishing nations of the world. On one trip to Canada, in the early 1960's, I once sailed nearly five miles through an almost continuous field of cod off the Grand Banks, a sight probably never to be seen again on a fish finder! Even in 1960, I recall that the average size of the cod catches at the Hull fish auction, in Britain, was often greater than a hand-span, which in my case is 68 inches. I wonder if we shall ever see cod of that size again? On another occasion, in 1957, we received a visit from Lt. Comdr. E.L. Pawsey, then a marine consultant with the famous consulting firm of Rendel, Palmer, and Tritton. I remember well, during his visit, that he pulled out a photograph of a Light Vessel which had broken adrift at the head of the Bay of Bengal, India, in the approaches of the River Hooghly. Light vessels are moored ships, designed to carry powerful signalling lights as a warning to other ships that there are rocks or similar navigational hazards in the vicinity. She had been torn from her moorings by a severe cyclone, and ended up some few miles *inland*, in the centre of an Indian village. He suggested that he would like our research efforts directed to prevent this sort of thing from happening again! Bearing in mind that severe cyclones in the area occur from June to November, that wind forces up to 90 miles per hour are prevalent, and that tidal waves under these cyclonic conditions, in the delta of the

RIDING QUALITIES OF LIGHT VESSELS

Figure 9   Photograph of a Light Vessel under test at N.P.L.

river, have been as high as 30 feet above datum, he seemed to be asking a lot! He then added that in 1942, the wind force was reported to have reached 130 miles per hour, and that *all* Light Vessels in the area had been swept from their stations. The pilot brig, sheltering nearby in the Saugor Roads, to the north of the delta, reported that under these conditions, in 1942, it was impossible to distinguish the surface of the water on account of a solid spray to a height of about 40 feet. His firm had been authorised to investigate the factors which lead to the parting of light vessels' cables and their uncomfortable riding behaviour, by the Commissioners for the Port of Calcutta, India. It was also intended that our research efforts should be directed towards the provision of greater safety of these vessels and their crews, since on many occasions the older vessels had broken adrift in less severe, but more frequent, storm conditions. There were some opinions available from the various officers of the Port Commissioners' older light vessels, which were used in the consideration of any new, replacement vessels. For example, there was a general belief on the station, that excessive rolling induced yaw, and undoubtedly, some of the older light vessels rolled heavily up to 20 degrees or more either way. In the strong currents of the River Hooghly, it appears likely that this opinion was correct. Double bilge keels were considered to be more effective than single ones. Their depth usually varied between 12 and 14 inches, and they were originally introduced to protect the bottom of these ships, if they broke adrift and were driven across the sands. It seems more likely that the lower bilge keel increased the directional stability of the ship, and that this indirectly reduced the roll. The heel of the stern post was believed to be the most vulnerable part of the ship if she was driven ashore, and this view was supported to some extent during the cyclone of 1942, when the rudder of one ship was driven *up through the upper deck*, and a second one was damaged. In another ship, the stem was damaged. (Ref.6) The use of a mizzen sail, which was discarded in 1916 when permanent awnings were fitted over the after deck, was considered by the older men to materially reduce the roll and pitch. L.V. "Hesperas", on the Mutlah Station, retained her mizzen sail until 1930. It appears likely that the fitting of the permanent awning aft had the same effect, to a lesser degree. In any case, it appears to be important that the centre of lateral resistance to wind, in the above water hull form, should be kept as far aft as possible. This was considered at the time, to be more and more difficult to achieve in the newer vessels, with the demand for more and better forward accommodation. There was a general belief amongst the crews, at that time, that composite-built, wooden ships were safer than those made only of steel. This feeling was so deep-seated, that unless a very great improvement in riding qualities could be attained in the new design, the change would be doomed to failure. Only two papers dealing with the behaviour of Light Vessels were found to have been published prior to 1955. (see Refs.7, 8) Based on their findings, the following valuable conclusions were drawn, which are still of assistance to authorities concerned with the operation of Light Vessels, even today.

- The normal length of the riding cable is 210 fathoms, and its diameter is 1-5/8 inches.
- "Tayco" steel cable is more satisfactory than iron.
- Deformation of links is not due to direct, but to indirect tensile strain, probably in the hawse pipes.
- Trinity House cables do not fail in service under direct tensile strain, but under shock load, which fractures the links.
- It is difficult to prove good welds in iron cable, except by over-straining the cable, which does it permanent harm and causes early deteroriation.

- The annealing of iron cables reduces the breaking strain. Steel cable does not need annealing for at least three years, but insufficient experience has been gained to state a definite period.
- It appears that the practice of condemning a cable on a reduction in diameter due to corrosion of 1/8 inch, is correct, and for strength purposes all cables should be considered for practical purposes to be 1-1/2 inches diameter, and not 1-5/8 inches, the size at which they are supplied.

Experience in Calcutta has proved the correctness of these conclusions, but until the steel Light Vessel was introduced, it was not possible to fit stud-link cable, on account of the galvanic action between the copper sheathing on the hull and the ship's cable. The cause of the fracture of cables was never traced in Calcutta, as in no case was part of the link recovered. It was noticeable, however, that the fracture nearly always took place near the ship, and that the "freshening" of the nip of the cable, i.e. the frequent relocation of the points of contact of the cable with the ship's hawse pipe, was considered of prime importance. After extensive discussion of all the foregoing considerations with the Clients, a full program of model experiments was agreed. (See Appendix 1). The experiments showed the marked benefits of providing a spring mechanism on the fore-deck of these vessels, to reduce the snatch load which comes on the cable, under extreme current conditions. From the point of view of safety and comfort, the new design is generally superior to the older vessels, the ship motions being reduced in amplitude, with longer pitching and rolling periods. Edward Pawsey, our leading co-author, passed away some years ago. He and I made regular enquiries about the light vessels on station in the mouth of the River Hooghly, especially about the L.V. "Flame", and *always* after each passing cyclone in the area! As far as I know, his wish that previous light vessel losses would not re-occur came to pass, and visitors from India always took great pleasure in informing us that she was still on station. This *practical* type of applied research was to be the fore-runner of many such experiences at N.P.L., and undoubtedly provided me with the investigative approach needed for forensic work in the marine field, which was to become a significant part of my later career in Canada.

One such very interesting project, for which we were retained by Clients, involved research into the behaviour of ships when berthing. The project consisted of testing a new patented device known as a "ring dolphin", shown in model form in Figure 18 This device consists of a large, hexagonal, ring buoy, which floats on the water surface and which is connected by a web-like structure to a steel collar, which is free to slide up and down a long steel cylinder. The cylinder is normally vertical, and attached at its lower end to steel feet, which work in a housing fixed to the sea or river bed. The cylinder is thus free to incline from the vertical position, by hinging from its bottom feet, whenever the ring dolphin is displaced from the original position. When an approaching ship makes contact with the dolphin, the dolphin is therefore moved from its original horizontal position, as shown in Figure 18., and inclines to a certain angle which depends mainly on the speed of contact and the displacement of the ship. Naturally, the movement of the dolphin produces a corresponding movement of the cylinder from the vertical, which then pivots about its lower feet, and introduces buoyancy forces on the cylinder tending to restore it to its original upright position. These buoyancy forces therefore resist the contact forces from the ship's side, as it slides along the ring dolphin, and have the effect of diverting the ship from its original direction before contact. Ring dolphins can therefore be of benefit when placed

Figure 18   Photograph of a Ring Dolphin under test at N.P.L.

strategically at dock entrances, or berths, where there are unusually high currents or cross winds. With the aid of such devices, the inventors also hoped that berthing ships, such as large tankers, would be less likely to require tug assistance and therefore be more under their own control, during the critical stages of making an approach to a restricted waterway or when entering a narrow dock. The N.P.L. experiments consisted of measuring the behaviour of a ring dolphin intended for the berthing of large tankers. The inclination of the long cylinder at various approach speeds and directions was recorded photographically by the Central Photographic Unit of the laboratory, as shown in Figure 18. The entire sequence of events, from the initial approach of the ship, the behaviour of the ship and the ring dolphin during impact, and the subsequent change of direction of the ship after impact, were also recorded. These experiments were considered highly satisfactory in our report, and also by the Clients, whose calculations of the behaviour of the ring dolphin under impact were largely substantiated. My only thought at the time was that many port authorities are rather zealous of their control of ships when berthing, particularly at oil terminals, and that they would perhaps regard this device as an intrusion on their normal tug operations. On the other hand, there are several ports which are notoriously difficult for berthing of ships, and which could obviously benefit from the installation of such ring dolphins, if placed at the approaches to these terminals, before the tugs take over the final berthing stages.

1957 was a noteworthy year for naval architects, and indeed a sad one for many. In that year, several well-known leaders in the hydrodynamic field passed away. Sir Richard William Lewis Gawn, C.B.E., D.Sc. R.C.N.C. (Dicky), Head of the Admiralty Experiment Works at Haslar, Gosport, for nearly two decades, passed away in July of that year. He

Life at N.P.L.

was at A.E.W. Haslar in 1945, the last year of my five-year apprenticeship, and took a great personal interest in the underwater, anti-mine work which I have already described. Again, just one month before, had come the sudden demise of James Foggo Allan, D.Sc. Head of the Ship Division of the National Physical Laboratory, Teddington, Middlesex, England, from 1948 until his death in 1957. He was the lead co-author of a paper in that year on "Yacht Testing", presented to the Royal Institution of Naval Architects.(see Ref. 9). Under his direction, I was responsible for yacht design and testing at the Ship Division of the N.P.L. and was co-author with B.E. Ware B.Eng. of that 1957 R.I.N.A. paper. Together, we devised a special dynamometer for the testing of yachts, which was done at the request of several representatives of the British Yachting Industry, in 1953. Prior to 1932, tank testing of model yachts was mainly confined to measuring their upright resistance, and using these results as a measure of quality of yacht performance. The misleading conclusions arrived at by the use of this procedure, when applying the results to the actual *heeled and yawed* motion of all sailing yachts, have been commented on by Professor K.S.M. Davidson (Ref.10). His pioneer work on yacht performance, and the many model tests conducted at the Stevens Institute of Technology, Hoboken, New Jersey, U.S.A., have proved that reliable prediction of full-scale yacht performance can be obtained, provided that sufficient care is taken in the experiments to avoid the occurrence of various flow phenomena, normally present during the testing of small models. In 1953, yacht testing was confined to just a few research facilities, the most notable being the Stevens Institute of Technology at Hoboken, already mentioned. The Stevens test method was to tow yacht models from two lateral dynamometers, which apply the corresponding component of the sail force, whilst permitting the model to assume its natural trim and

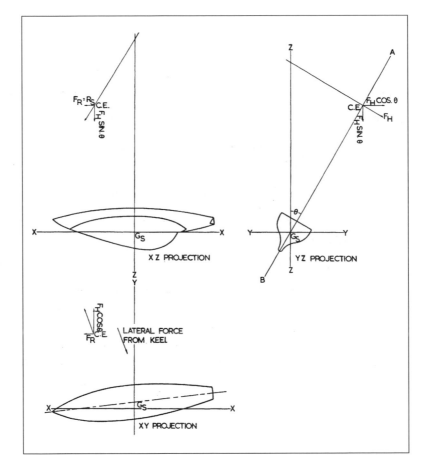

Figure 7   Diagram of forces acting on a sailing yacht, when "close-hauled" on the port tack (note the heel and yaw).

heel, without interfering with measurement of the model's longitudinal resistance. The longitudinal resistance of the model was measured on a separate dynamometer. This method is still in use, and has been used in the successful development of several famous yachts which raced in the World Cup series. Dr. G. Kempf, once Head of the Hamburg Research laboratory in Germany, had also devised a method for the testing of yacht models about that time. His method was to simulate the effect of the wind force on a model hull, by applying longitudinal and lateral forces to the model, at the "centre of effort" position, i.e. the position where the total sail force is assumed to act, using a system of falling weights and pulleys. (see Fig.7) Under the action of these combined forces, the model was found to assume a stable heeled and yawed position, and to advance at a certain speed, which depended on its hull form characteristics. It was thus an easy way to compare the behaviour of two different models, under the action of a constant relative wind force. The author did not, however, claim that his method was as reliable as that employed at the Stevens Institute. About the same time, Mr. J. Marshall, North Hayling, Hampshire in the U.K., designed and built a special dynamometer for the testing of yachts. This ingenious apparatus consisted essentially of a five-component balance, to which the model is rigidly attached. Unfortunately, although useful results can be obtained with this type of instrumentation, the fact that the model is not free to assume a natural vertical equilibrium position, as occurs on the full scale, severely limits its use as a commercial instrument. Model tests on yacht forms were also conducted at Genoa University, Italy, by Professor de Bella, in the early fifties. The models were fitted with sails, and their performance compared in constant, simulated wind conditions. In addition, the models were also compared by direct measurement of their resistance and lateral forces, by means of a dynamometer.

The Naval Architect

The N.P.L. dyanamometer was designed and built in the Ship Division, as a research tool, and also for commercial yacht testing.(See Appendix 2). In the late 1950's and early 1960's, several well-known yacht designers including Charles Nicholson, used the N.P.L. facilities and had yacht tests conducted for their Clients at the Ship Division of the N.P.L., at Teddington. Notable amongst these was Sir Owen Aisher, whose famous series of yachts under the name "Yeoman", starting with Yeoman I, often made the news in the yachting magazines of that era. Several other notables, including foreign royalty, also had their latest designs tested at the Ship Division of the N.P.L. at that time. As part of the yacht research program, we also made full scale tests of a 5.5 metre class yacht, conducted on the nearby King George V reservoir, to measure the "speed made good" against the wind, for comparison with the corresponding model predictions. The results showed that the optimum full scale performance was in close agreement with the model predictions, except at higher wind speeds, when the full scale performance is lower than predicted, probably on account of gusty wind conditions and the effects of waves, which are not simulated in the model tests. During the discussion of our N.P.L. paper, (Ref. 9), Mr. W.A. Crago (Bill), then Head of the Saunders-Roe Tank at Cowes, on the Isle of Wight, showed a very interesting film of their new yacht-testing apparatus. This was originally based on the same N.P.L. methods and techniques already described, but became modified in the light of experience to suit their own special requirements at Saunders-Roe. Several other well-known yachting authorities and enthusiasts joined in the discussion of our N.P.L. paper, and those interested in sailing can still learn a lot from their remarks. About that time, I met Alfred Hiley, a Cumbrian, a wonderful man then in his eighties and a world famous Civil Engineer. In fact, his papers and formulae on how to calculate the forces and power required when driving "piles", used in the foundations of many buildings and other structures are still used to this day. His works can be found in almost any book on civil engineering, of that period and before. In the discussion of our R.I.N.A. yacht paper (Ref. 9), he described some earlier tests he had conducted at Ramsden Dock, Barrow-in-Furness, which were based on a test method first developed by Lt. Col. Thomas English. These are described in the proceedings of the Institution of Mechanical Engineers in 1896. (Ref. 30). The method is extremely simple for comparing the performance of two yachts in the close-hauled condition, i.e. against the wind. By adjusting the lateral position of the towing point between the two models, so that they are in equilibrium, it is an easy matter to determine the relative resistance of each hull form. He quoted several test results for model yachts, which had demonstrated their superiority in club races, using this technique. I spent many happy times with Alfred Hiley, visiting his home at Rickmansworth, Hertfordshire, with its beautiful gardens, especially since his interests and expertise were so far ranging. He was a keen botanist, an apiarist, as well as an inventor of many ingenious engineering devices, so that I learned a lot in his company about many things. We became close friends, right up until his sudden departure from this earthly abode in the early sixties, not so long before my departure to Canada, where I was able to extend and apply some of his ideas in practice.

In 1958, a very interesting paper by D. Phillips-Birt, Associate member of the Royal Institution of Naval Architects, London, was presented on the subject of yacht measurement. (see Ref. 11). This paper was very timely, and provided the opportunity for discussion of the various measurement rules which govern the design of several classes of yachts. These included the International 5.5 Metre Class, many designs of which we tested at the N.P.L., also the International 7, 8, 9, 10.5 and 12 Metre Cruiser Racer Classes, and those to the Royal Ocean Racing Club rule. During the discussion, Mr. James McGruer, Associate Member, pointed out that the rule of the Cruising Club of America, (C.C.A.) and the International Racing Rule (I.R.R.) for yachts under 14.1/2 metres had unfortunately not been included. In his valuable contribution, however, he did show how the C.C.A and I.R.R. rules have influenced the other rules discussed in the paper. As subsequent events have now shown, the various international challenges for the America's Cup and the wide variety of yacht designs produced under the I.R.R. rule for yachts under 14.1/2 metres, have had a strong influence on yacht design all over the world. These include such hull form effects as those of changes in beam, draft, and length, centre board and keel design, and even extend to sail design parameters, such as aspect ratio and centre of effort. (see Nomenclature)

The British Ship Research Association, then with its headquarters in London, worked very closely with the Ship Division of the N.P.L. at Teddington, on a wide range of marine research projects. Many of these projects were concerned with finding the effects of hull form on ship resistance and propulsion, both in calm water and in waves. The results of these model experiments, both at the N.P.L and later at the Vickers Limited, Ship Model Tank, at St. Albans, were presented by the staff of these organisations to the Royal Institution of Naval Architects, London, U.K., and other similar learned institutions. (see Refs.12-16). This research is invaluable to ship designers when estimating ship performance, especially in the early design stages. The effects on engine power requirements at various ship speeds can therefore be determined for a wide range of hull forms, in this case extending from those with block coefficients from 0.55 to 0.88. *(Block coefficient is a ratio, defined by the displacement,divided by the triple product of length, beam and mean draft.).*

This range of ship fullness covers such ships as medium-speed, dry cargo liners, tankers and bulk carriers. Most of the models tested were of actual ships, and the results can therefore be used by designers to assess the additional effects of practical design changes in the position of the centre of buoyancy, forward and aft, the beam and the draft. As a result of several lunchtime discussions with my friend and colleague, J. Geoffrey Hayes, of the Mathematics Division of the N.P.L., I became aware of the powerful uses which can be made of statistical theory, in the analysis of model experimental work. In addition to the published results for such tests as the B.S.R.A. methodical series, described above, there already existed a vast store of resistance and propulsion data, for actual ships of all kinds. These are generally unrelated, except in a generic way, but they do contain the results of many design changes made in hull form, by various ship designers throughout the world. As such, they show the historical development and relative merits of the various hull forms and propeller systems used over the years. Since I had already assembled the whole of the previous N.P.L. data for fishing vessels, over several decades, and had added many of my own more recent results, I decided to analyse them using multi-dimensional, statistical theory. Those interested to learn more about such statistical analyses, can study them in greater detail in References (18-23, &55). I thus became the first one to successfully apply these statistical techniques to ship design. Working closely with my friend Geoff. Hayes, some 150 or more model resistance results were analysed, using multi-curvilinear regression analysis. Six hull form parameters were used, which I had already found to play a predominant role in fishing vessel design, as the basis of the analysis. As a measure of ship resistance I also found that the Telfer criterion (see Ref.18), was the best one to use, when comparing the various hull forms at constant speed-length ratio. In other words, when the ship speed, divided by the square root of the length of the vessel, is constant, the Telfer criterion expresses the *quality* of the hull forms in terms of their resistance per ton of displacement. The first regression equation, containing 30 terms based on these six parameters, was found to be within 3.0 per cent of those measured in 95 per cent of the cases, and within 5.0 per cent for 99 per cent, at the various speed length ratios, $(V/L^{0.5})$ from 0.80 to 1.10. In the final analysis, the accuracy of a regression equation, containing 32 terms, was obtained within 1/10 knot for over 95% of the data, at all speeds, which is more than sufficient for all practical design purposes. Having deduced a regression equation which predicts all the previous resistance data, we then decided to optimise the equation, to see if there were any further improvements indicated. Four models were designed and tested according to the hull form parameters suggested by the mathematical optimisation. When compared with best modern practice at that time, in 1958, I found that all the newly-optimised designs, derived from the statistical analysis, gave results better than any of the best ones previously obtained. (see Ref. 17 pp.363). The greatest reductions in resistance applied to the fullest hull form, and showed more than 22 per cent improvement.(see Figure 10) Working with T.P. O.'Brien, also of the Ship Division N.P.L. and Geoff Hayes, I extended the analysis to include all the propulsion results available for a wide range of trawler forms, previously tested at the NP.L. From the regression equation developed, we found that the propulsive efficiency for these vessels depends mainly on three important parameters, viz. the thickness ratio of the propeller, the rudder thickness ratio, and the advance coefficient. This latter coefficient is defined as the speed of the ship, divided by the

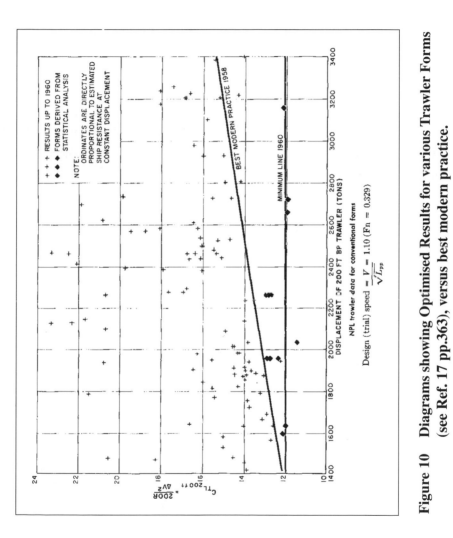

Figure 10 Diagrams showing Optimised Results for various Trawler Forms (see Ref. 17 pp.363), versus best modern practice.

product of the diameter of the propeller and its number of revolutions per second. Prediction of the propulsive coefficients for all models tested was achieved within a standard error of 1.45 per cent, which is generally within the accuracy of repeatability of these tests. The regression equation revealed some interesting conclusions, notably that certain parameters, such as the advance coefficient and the rudder thickness ratio, should be increased in value for optimum efficiency. On the other hand, the equation showed that the thickness ratio of the propeller should be reduced as much as possible, to improve the propulsive efficiency, which of course has been confirmed in practice. In 1962, I published some additional propulsion results for three optimised trawler forms of varying fullness.(see Ref.23). These showed that the improvements in resistance, obtained for these optimised forms, had been achieved without any penalty in propulsive efficiency. (see Figures 11,12). In fact, as can be seen in Figure 11, the propulsive coefficients of these optimised hulls are superior to many of the best of those previously existing vessels actually in service. Following on the obviously successful application of these statistical techniques to ship design, the Food and Agriculture Organisation of the United Nations requested that we analyse all the fishing vessel results which they had gathered together from sources all over the world. Mr. Jan-Olof Traung, Chief, Fishing Vessel Section, Department of Fisheries, F.A.O., then arranged for me to work at their facilities in Rome, on secondment from N.P.L., and to prepare a detailed proposal for the analysis of their fishing vessel data. This proved to be a most enjoyable and stimulating experience, not least being the opportunity it provided to sample the excellent Roman cuisine! We also found time at the week-ends, to visit the golf club at Mount Fiuggi, not so far from Rome, where many of the staff of F.A.O. were members, and where international rivalries were often settled in

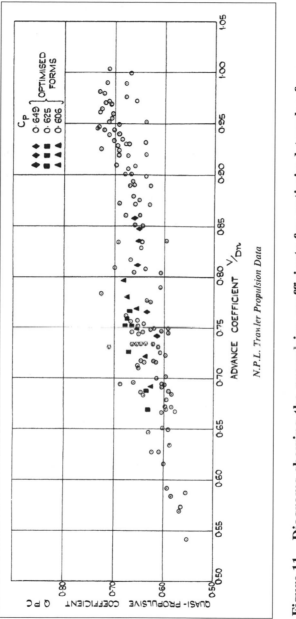

Figure 11   Diagrams showing the propulsive coefficients for optimised trawler forms, versus best modern practice.

an agreeable manner. I made many friends whilst working there, Jan-Olof Traung, Tsutomu Tsuchiya, Norio Fujinami, Bob Hamlisch, Peter Gurtner, to name but a few, and was thus able to study all available resistance data with them, which included results from many of the leading hydrodynamic research laboratories throughout the world.

These included the following:

The Hydraulic Laboratory, Division of Mechanical Engineering, National Research Council, Ottawa, Canada

Bassin d'Essais de Carènes, Paris, France

Institut für Schiffsbau, Berlin-Karlshorst

Hamburgische Schiffbau Versuchsanstalt, Hamburg, Germany

Versuchsanstalt für Wasserbau und Schiffsbau, Berlin

Vasca Nazionale per le Experienze di Architettura Navale, Rome

Fishing Boat Laboratory, Fisheries Agency, Tokyo, Japan

Ned. Scheepsbouwkundig Proefstation, Wageningen, The Netherlands

Skipsmodelltanken, Norges Tekniske Högskole, Trondheim, Norway

Canal de Experiencias Hidrodinámicas, Madrid, Spain

Kungl. Tekniska Högskolan, Stockholm, Sweden

Swedish State Shipbuilding Experimental Tank, Goteborg, Sweden

William Denny Bros. Ltd. (Experimental Tank), Dumbarton, Scotland,

National Physical Laboratory, Teddington, Middlesex, England

Davidson Tank, Stevens Institute of Technology, Hoboken, New Jersey, U.S.A.

The Naval Tank, Department of Naval Architecture and Marine Engineering, University of Michigan, Ann Arbor, U.S.A.

David W. Taylor Model Basin, Navy Department, Washington, D.C.

Webb Towing Tank, Webb Insititute of Naval Architecture, Glen Cove, Long Island, New York, U.S.A.

A preliminary assessment of the data was made by my friend Tsuchiya, of the Japanese Fishing Boat Laboratory, Tokyo, and now head of that renowned establishment. Large variations in resistance per ton of displacement were found between the best and the worst hull forms included in the F.A.O. analysis. In this situation, as with the original N.P.L. data for the larger stern trawlers, the possibility of detecting the effects of changes in individual hull parameters, by statistical methods, becomes even more attractive. As there were many more model results available, it was also possible to include additional hull parameters allowing for their wider shape variations. My earlier experience with fishing vessel design at the N.P.L. suggested that the maximum angles of "run" of the waterlines and of the buttock slope, in the after-body, played some part in determining their overall resistance. (detailed definitions, and a full description of the analysis are given Refs. 21, 22). Geoff Hayes, Tsuchiya and I were therefore able to develop a regression equation which consisted of 86 terms, based on a total of nine hull form parameters. (Ref.21) The coefficients in the regression equation were determined using the principle of "least squares", for each of eleven speed to length ratios, $(V/L^{0.5})$, so that the power-speed curve for any particular hull shape and dimensions, could be estimated from the lines plan of the vessel, to a high order of accuracy. Again working closely with Geoff. Hayes and the staff of the Mathematics Division of the N.P.L., we then made a mathematical optimisation of the data, for fishing vessels having lengths of 40, 55, 70 and 85 feet, which covers the practical size range for these vessels. Hulls were designed and tested, corresponding to these optimised hull parameters, the 40 and 55 foot vessels being F.A.O. designs, the 70 footer being an N.P.L. design, and the largest 85 footer being designed at the Chalmers Technical Institute, Gothenburg, Sweden. (see Figure 12 & Ref.22). The resistance results for all four designs were found to be better than all previous

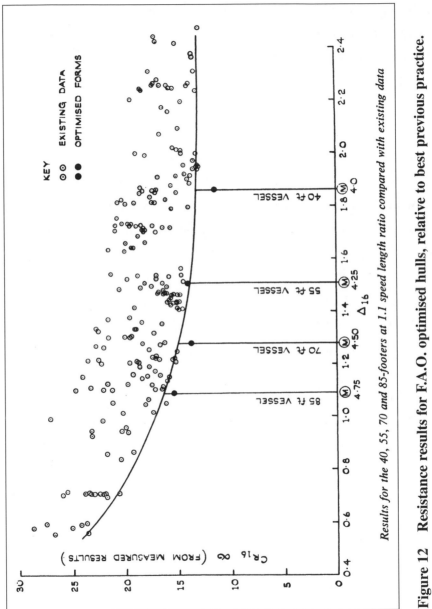

Results for the 40, 55, 70 and 85-footers at 1.1 speed length ratio compared with existing data

Figure 12 Resistance results for F.A.O. optimised hulls, relative to best previous practice.

designs of fishing vessels, and therefore confirmed, once again, that this statistical approach provides a powerful design tool for designers. Since ship resistance is directly related to engine power requirements, important reductions in horse power were thus found to be possible, by making suitable changes in hull form and dimensions. For a typical fishing fleet, these power reductions can amount to many millions of dollars. Subsequent events, after I had emigrated to Canada, were to show how well these methods were appreciated by those in the fishing industry, long after 1959, when my first paper on this subject was published in Fishing Boats of the World 2. (Ref. 18) During the course of working closely with the staff of F.A.O. in Rome, in preparation for their 1959 Conference on Fishing Vessels, I met Bob Hamlisch, a very well-known economist, then working in the Economics Branch of the F.A.O. I found that we had many interests in common, ranging from Italian paintings and other local objets d'art, to classical music and fine cuisine, extending also to a keen interest in the application of statistical methods to fisheries economic problems. Since I was already working with several major fishing companies in the U.K., and analysing their technical and economic data on a confidential basis, I naturally became even more interested in this aspect of the F.A.O. work, in which Bob Hamlisch played a leading role.(see Ref. 27). In September 1964, F.A.O. held a meeting on "Business Decisions in Fishery Industries", which was very well attended by 90 participants and observers from 28 countries, and two international organisations. I was invited to write a paper on the relative importance of trawler design in the economics of fishery operations (see Ref. 24), and acted as rapporteur for the Session on the choice of optimum type of fishing vessel, under the Chairmanship of Prof. G.M. Gerhardsen. of the Institute of Fisheries Economics, Bergen, Norway. Bob Hamlisch's paper was specially aimed at ways to expand the world store of statistical and economic information, needed for decision-making in fishery industries. He pointed out that even with the rapid development of electronic data processing at that time, the fishing industry was far behind the agricultural industry, and others, in making management decisions based on the analysis of such information. The collection of properly-indexed fisheries data was therefore considered of prime importance by F.A.O., in order to make more informed investment and operational decisions in the fishing industry. Events in the European fisheries were happening at that time, which gave grave cause for concern to many fishing vessel owners of that era, and rightly so. In the early sixties, fish catches were already starting to decrease in size and abundance. Catches of fresh fish landed on ice, caught by the distant water fleets, were also getting to be more and more difficult to land in prime condition. With a practical edible limit of about 16 days, the time spent on the fishing grounds had to be limited in order to reach the home ports in good time, otherwise quality and therefore price at the fish auctions were found to suffer. This led naturally to an emphasis on top speed performance, since the first catches to be landed at the home ports produced the highest prices. At that time therefore, most of the leading trawler Owners in the U.K. and some in France, insisted on having their latest vessels Tank tested at the Ship Division of the N.P.L., and they were naturally very pleased when their ships headed the list of top earners for the year.

A preliminary techno-economic analysis of some company results was made at the N.P.L., about that time, (Ref.31) and showed some rather surprising results. When the catches for each fishing vessel were also identified by their skippers, the analysis showed that greater company profitability could be achieved, if the traditional practice of allocating the latest vessel to the best current skipper was replaced with a different system. For example, group profitability could be significantly improved, if the best skipper ran the third best vessel, and the fourth best skipper ran the best vessel, and so on down through the fleet, with each skipper running different vessels from those which they traditionally operated. Although the results of the statistical analysis were accepted by the fishing vessel owners, it proved very difficult for them to change the old tradition, whereby the best skipper *always* expected to get the latest vessel in the fleet.

This type of statistical analysis, for example, can also be used to compare relative yacht performance, since races are won and lost, not just by the design characteristics of yachts and their sails, but by the skill of their skippers. In the mid sixties, the British distant water fishing fleet commenced a new interesting phase of development, which had been somewhat fore-shadowed earlier by the fishing fleets of Spain, Portugal, Japan, Russia and others, who had traditionally caught their fish at greater distances from their home ports, and therefore required to pay more attention to the preservation of the catch. I refer of course to the new breed of stern trawlers, designed to freeze and sometimes process their catches. Techno-economic analyses of requirements for such freezer trawlers (Ref.26), showed that important dimensional and other changes such as speed and hold capacity, were required for the new vessels, compared to the older, traditional, fresh fish catchers. Figures 13 and 14, for example, show the effects on economic efficiency of changes in ship speed, fish price, catch rate and fullness of some of these vessels. Such pre-investment, techno-economic studies for fisheries enterprises then became of increasing importance in the industry, when it became better realised that returns on invested capital must be competitive with other shore-based industries. Failure to appreciate these requirements prevented investment funds being diverted into many fishing operations at

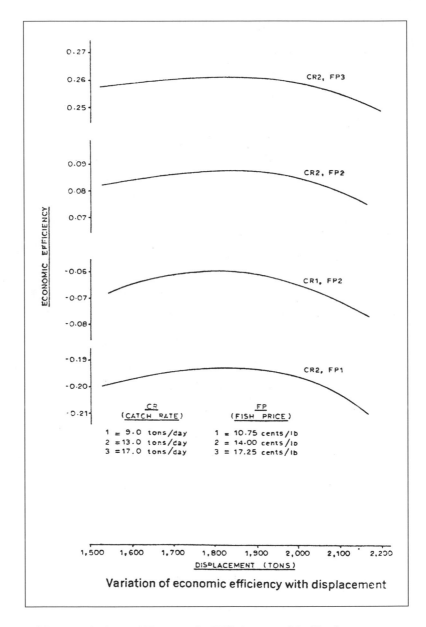

Variation of economic efficiency with displacement

Figure 13   Variation of Economic Efficiency with displacement.

that time. Furthermore, as the freezer type fishing vessels became more complex and required larger amounts of capital, the individual resources of some companies engaged in fishing operations tended to be squeezed, to such an extent that their healthy growth was inhibited. Techno-economic methods applied to these fishing operations could therefore demonstrate to potential investors what returns on capital outlay could be expected. By simulating the intended fishing operations mathematically, preliminary estimates of economic efficiency were made for many hundreds, even thousands of possible alternatives, each of which was technically viable. All of the required inputs to these analyses such as shipbuilding costs for different vessel sizes, maintenance and repair costs, crew wages, insurance and related data, catch data, fish prices, running and other operational costs, were made available by the propective owners, or derived from other data sources. Figure 13 shows the variations of economic efficiency with ship displacement for a new series of refrigerated stern trawlers varying in length between 44 and 68 metres. One very important fact emerged from this work, since it was found that for this particular class of freezer trawler, the optimum displacement for changes in fish price and catching rate, did not change very much and was between 1800 and 1900 tons. The ship speed requirements were also quite different from those for the fresh fish vessels, since the most economic speed was found to be in the region of 12 knots, mainly because there was no longer any need to return to home port at excessive speeds, typically around 17.0 knots, to meet the opening of the market.

The 1959 Conference on Fishing Boats of the World 2, organised by the Food and Agriculture Organisation of the United Nations, (F.A.O.) Rome, Italy provided an international forum for a wide range of experts to discuss such topics as ship construction, their behaviour at sea, and

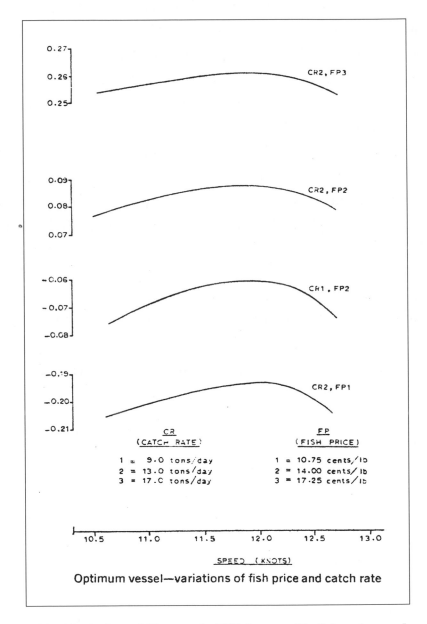

Figure 14   Variation of Economic Efficiency with fish price and catch rate.

vessel productivity. As one of the authors, I presented a paper on the subject of trawler forms with bulbous bows (Ref.28), which was the first to show the effects of such bows on vessels working at relatively high speed-length ratios of about $V/L^{0.50}=1.20$, in smooth *and* rough water. Resistance and propulsion experiments were therefore conducted in calm water and in waves. Two models were compared, one being of a conventional deep sea trawler, and the other with a bulbous bow, having the same overall dimensions and displacement. Propulsion tests were made for each form, with N.P.L. propellers suitable for free-running and trawling conditions. These comparisons showed that overall reductions in power between 10 and 15% were obtained with the bulbous bow form in calm water, and that the bulbous bow design suffered a smaller reduction in speed than did the conventionl design, for the same resistance. As a result of these and other similar tests which followed, many fishing vessels were constructed with bulbous bows, not only in the U.K., but in countries such as Spain, Portugal, Canada, Poland, Japan and several other fishing countries throughout the world.

Perhaps because of the difficulties in observing the flow *around* ship models, there was and is a paucity of information on that subject. The small amount of information which did exist in 1961, was confined to the flow over the *surface* of the models tested, and that usually involved visualisation of the flow by means of ejecting coloured dyes from inside the model. Sometimes also the flow over hull surfaces, such as brackets or skegs, was observed by painting a dye on them and observing the patterns which were formed by the water as it flowed over these appendages.(see Fig.22) Neither method provided any actual measurements of the local fluid velocity, nor did the method cover the region around the hull, away from the surface. I then conceived the idea that the problem might be solved photographically, using particles of neutral buoyancy, and discussed the matter with my old friend Charles Guthrie, head of the Central Photographic Unit of the N.P.L. Particles of a special polystyrene about 0.20 inches in diameter were made, which after some experimentation could be produced in quantity, each having neutral buoyancy in fresh water. The Ministry of Works and the Central Photographic Unit of the N.P.L. then designed a special unit which controlled twin Newman-Sinclair synchronised ciné cameras, which could be operated under water. The particles of neutral buoyancy, up to 12 in number for each experiment, are ejected ahead of the advancing model, and their subsequent motion is recorded in the regions of the hull at which the three-dimensional velocity field is required. A cluster of particles is usually ejected and viewed in two planes at right angles by the twin synchronous 35 mm. ciné cameras, shooting through matching inverted periscopes. (see Figure 15) The two synchronised film strips obtained are analysed frame by frame on a Film Analyser, which records the Cartesian co-ordinates of each particle throughout the motion, in the form of a punched tape. This information is subsequently analysed on a high speed digital computer. A program was prepared with my co-author, Miss V.A. Daniels of the Mathematics Division, N.P.L., which evaluates the velocity components of the flow, for specific co-ordinates in the region covered by the observations. In cases where flow reversal or other peculiarities of the flow are likely to occur, the two film records may be projected in the usual manner and studied at leisure. The flow over stern appendages such as open shafts, brackets and bossings can also be obtained in a similar fashion. This technique proved to be very successful, and much superior to the old visual method of injecting coloured dye into the boundary layer flow over the hull surface, which did not provide any quantitative results, and was also superior to the quantitative method of measuring the flow velocity

SCHEMATIC ARRANGEMENTS FOR FLOW DETECTION

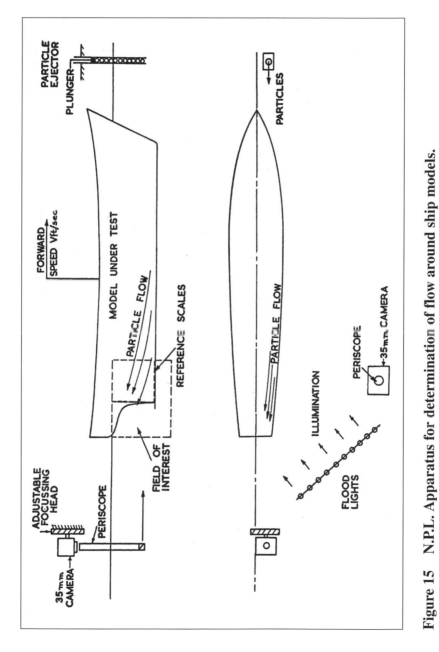

Figure 15   N.P.L. Apparatus for determination of flow around ship models.

by means of pitot tubes, which can cause unwanted interference effects between the models and the apparatus, and in any case does not give reliable results close to the hull surface.

I hope that at this stage of my narrative, the reader will have started to gain some insight into the work of a naval architect, *specialised in hydrodynamics*. This of course was my *first* career, before emigrating to Canada in 1966, and getting into the "nuts and bolts" of ship design and construction, ship repair and maintenance. The last few years at N.P.L., before 1966, were very memorable, and led to many subsequent changes in the lives of those working there. There were also some special note-worthy events! For example, one week-end, I was designated to be in charge of the Ship Division during the making of a film called "The Dam Busters". During World War 2, the famous inventor, Barnes Wallis, had used the tank facilities in the Ship Division for the testing of his design of spherical bomb, which was deployed in the attacks by the Royal Air Force on the famous Eider Dam, which supplied the hydro electric power for a large part of the German war industries in that region. As those who saw the film will remember, the only way to attack the dam successfully, was to make a low level approach, releasing the bomb at a pre-determined distance and altitude from the dam face. The success of the operation depended on the bomb making a series of skipping impacts as it rolled towards the dam, *the last impact being at the dam face*, such that the bomb fell to the bottom of the dam and then exploded. I understand that this technique has since been made into a game! The design of the dam was very robust, and it had been determined beforehand by British Intelligence that any other type of aerial attack would be ineffective in breaking it, and thus unable to release the enormous body of water contained inside the dam. That weekend the whole bombing test procedure was to be repeated in the

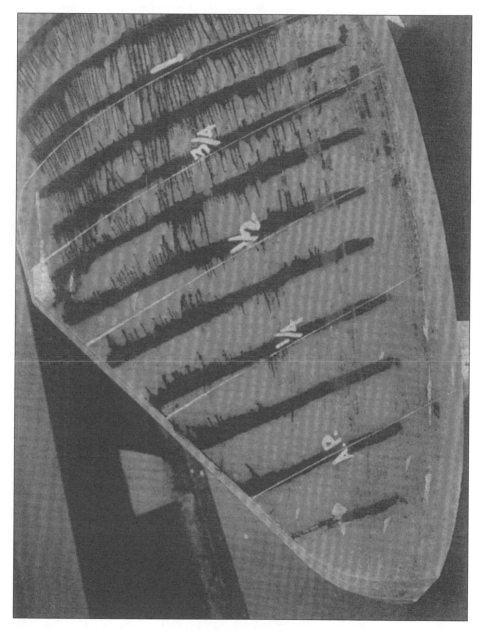

Figure 22   Flow over model surface by N.P.L. dye tests.

The Naval Architect

Number 1 Tank of the Ship Division, N.P.L. Barnes Wallis was on hand to advise on the test procedure, and I remember that the lead actor who played his part in the film so well, was Michael Redgrave. After some rather disappointing attempts to simulate the skipping of the bomb on the water surface, the model tests were made with sufficient accuracy to reproduce the desired effects. The model bomb then made the correct number of skips on the water surface, before arriving at the face of the dam, making contact, and then dropping to the bottom of the dam. Once again photography played its part, at the same scene where we had conducted the previous tests on the light vessels! On other occasions, I recall that we always enjoyed the visits of such personages as the Duke of Edinburgh, The Prince Philip, the King of Sweden, King Haakon of Norway, and even well known Russian personalities such as Kruschov and Gorbachev. All showed a keen interest in our work and asked many searching questions, showing that they really appreciated the purpose of such facilities and their usefulness in marine research.

In 1957 a paper was presented by James Foggo Allan, D.Sc., to the Royal Insitution of Naval Architects which described the new ship hydrodynamics laboratory, then under construction at Feltham, Middlesex, in the U.K. (Ref. 32) These test facilities consisted of a main tank having dimensions of 1,300 feet long, 48 feet wide, and 25 feet deep.with a top carriage speed of 50 feet per second. The tank was also fitted with a wave maker, capable of generating waves 40 feet long and 2 feet high. There was also a manoeuvring tank 100 feet long by 100 feet wide and 8 feet deep, in which radio controlled models could be tested in calm water and in waves. The monstrous water tunnel, 44 inches in diameter, with a top speed of 50 feet per second, was 180 feet in depth, mostly below ground. Bill Crago, then Head of the Saunders Roe Tank, at Cowes, I.O.W. was the first to point out *the enormous economic*

penalties in choosing such a large depth of water tunnel, although unfortunately, at that time, the construction of the building was in progress. (see discusion of Ref.32) This propeller testing facility was the design and detailed planning responsibility of A. Silverleaf, of the Ship Division, and according to the discussions on the paper by Allan (Ref. 32) the design work and detailed planning of the main towing and manoeuvring tanks was the responsibility of J. R. Shearer. The original budgeted cost estimates for the whole project were around 2.0 million pounds sterling, which included a tank length of 1,800 feet and a width of 50 feet. Unfortunately, later estimates in 1952 showed that the actual cost would likely exceed 3.0 million pounds sterling, a more than 50% increase from the original figure. This level of expenditure was unacceptable, and means therefore had to be taken to reduce the length of the tank by some 500 feet and to reduce the width of the tank from 50 to 48 feet, and to construct the tank above ground level, as shown in Figure 16, to get back to the originally approved figure of 2.0 million pounds. Unfortunately, no attempt was made to cut the cost of the water tunnel, by reducing its depth of 180 feet below ground, nor was it fully appreciated, as pointed out by Bill Crago, just how much this depth was so completely out of line with all previous facilities. Neverthless, approval was given to proceed with the building of these modified facilities at Feltham, and they were opened in 1959. **Unfortunately, partly due to their predictable, enormous, running and mainte-nance costs, and the reduced test requirements of the world shipping industry since they were built, they were closed down in December, 1987 and bull-dozed to the ground in March, 1988.**
I resigned from the Ship Division of the N.P.L. in 1966 in order to accept an offer of partnership in Canada, with a commercial firm of naval architects and marine engineers. My decision was also based on a

NATIONAL PHYSICAL LABORATORY:
NEW SHIP HYDRODYNAMICS LABORATORY

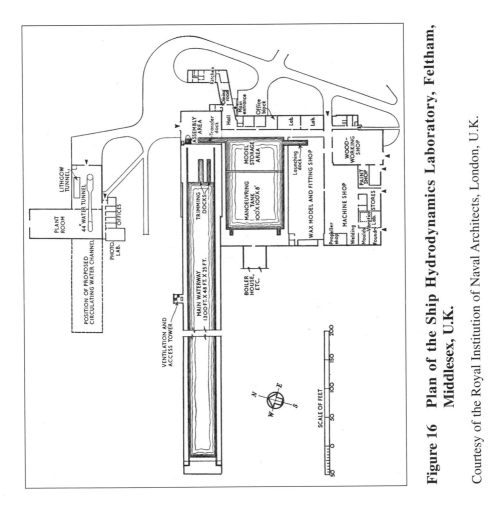

Figure 16 Plan of the Ship Hydrodynamics Laboratory, Feltham, Middlesex, U.K.

Courtesy of the Royal Institution of Naval Architects, London, U.K.

general dissatisfaction with the way in which the Feltham project was mishandled, the lack of appreciation by those responsible that such facilities *must* be designed to pay their way, by performing applied research for industry, and the general lack of staff confidence we had in the ability of those transient heads, who seemed to use the Ship Division in particular, and the N.P.L. generally, as means for their own personal agrandissement. It was almost regarded as a standard joke at the time, that newly-appointed directors of the N.P.L. just stayed long enough to get their knighthood, before moving on! It therefore came as no surprise to hear later that many of my friends and colleagues had followed my lead, and taken up appointments elsewhere in the shipping industry, including other research facilities and universities. This was no doubt due in part to the pressures which came on the remaining research staff, as those responsible for the upkeep of the new facilities higher up the ladder, came to appreciate the enormity of the problems they had inherited from the original, badly conceived, design concept, and the lack of a secured, commercial, research income. A review of the world marine research facilities at that time in 1957 shows that there were only 6 tanks with lengths in excess of 1,000 feet, and that the total number below 1,000 feet length was 47, many of those being less than 200 feet in length. None of those facilities in excess of 1,000 feet length were noted for their *commercial or economic* viability, being mainly operated to conduct marine research on military projects, and it therefore should have come as no surprise to anyone with any business acumen, that the Feltham project was a financial disaster in the making.

Dr. F. H. Todd who had been appointed to make a world survey of the various tank testing facilities back in 1945, and later, seems to have convinced authorities at the time that Britain needed new test facilities on such a grand scale, and the die was then cast for those following on to perpetuate the folly. Ironically, he came back briefly in 1958 for a few years, to head the Ship Division of the N.P.L. at Teddington, where he had originally worked, and then returned back to the naval establishment at David Taylor Model Basin in Washington, D.C. where the largest marine research facilities in the world are still located! It would be most interesting to learn just how much those naval facilities are used, and how much they cost to run on an annual basis, and whether similar economic data were ever used as input into the decision to build the research facilities at Feltham, Middlesex, in the early 1950's. Perhaps, as the pioneering hydrodynamicist William Froude had discovered a century ago, **smaller is better**, when it comes to performing marine research on a commercial basis. I now understand, regrettably, that No.1 and No.2 Test Tanks, and the other marine research facilities at Teddington suffered a similar fate to those at Feltham, and were eventually demolished early in May, 1998, some ten years after the Feltham affair. After all the valuable research work performed at Ship Division, N.P.L. over the better part of this century, it seems such a shame that those facilities had to end in such an ignominious fashion, despite all the brave attempts made to keep them operative. Fortunately, much of the N.P.L. ship research data still remains on record, and was also published in several learned institutions throughout the world. All can draw on that published material which still has practical application, even to this day.

CHAPTER IV

OFF TO CANADA

I departed from Southampton in early August, 1966 on the Canadian Steamships liner the "Empress of Canada", bound for Montreal. As I had already done some work for Canadian Pacific whilst at the N.P.L., I was afforded some special privileges, one of them being to sit at the Captain's table, and the other was to be able to visit the bridge and chat with the ship's officers. I recall that one of the party sitting at the captain's table was a charming lady, Viscountess Weir, whose family owned major shares in the mining company called Inco. She was visiting Canada with her daughter, and gave me a lot of good advice on how to best succeed in Canada, when she found out that I was about to start on a new career in Montreal. I am still thankful for it, and was so sorry to learn of her untimely passing away some years afterwards. The trip was relatively uneventful, except for the last few days when we came through some stormy weather near Cape Race, as we neared the estuary of the St. Lawrence River. Sailing up-stream we passed Anticosti Island, then Tadoussac, at the mouth of the Saguenay River, and saw the mink whales, seals and all kinds of sea life in great abundance. Both Anticosti and Tadoussac were later to play a significant role in my life as a marine consultant. The ship landed first at Quebec City, where we were cleared for customs and immigration, and then proceeded up river to Montreal. What a sight to see at that time, the port full of large ships of all kinds, a thriving metropolis, the year before Expo '67., when it seemed that everything was alive and well, so dynamic, and there was so much to do. Whatever happened? I think we all know, but few will say, at least not out loud! I often wonder whether those good old days will ever return to Montreal. Perhaps they will, when we are finally rid of those few remaining, *self-serving, parochial, xenophobic, bigots* who want to stifle its dynamicism, its truly international flavour, its joie de vivre, panache, and diversity of languages, cuisine, art and literature, and resent its more favourable advances into the next millenium. Quebec sait faire?

CHAPTER V

THE EARLY DAYS OF EXPO '67 -AND BEYOND

My first year in business in Montreal, the year before Expo '67, was full of surprises, as up to that time I had virtually no previous commercial background or experience. I was a research scientist, trained to solve problems which arise in the design and operation of ships. I was then a *specialist*, designing hull forms, propellers, rudders, and other ship propulsion devices, supervising the many resistance, propulsion, and manoeuvring tests already described in the earlier chapters, and later checking them out on full scale ship trials. This work often extended to checking the plans of other ship and propeller designers, some of whom are now no longer practising.

However, I soon learned that the cash register did not ring with quite the same regularity as in the old days at the N.P.L, that clients had to be courted and did not just appear on the doorstep of the office, as before, in a never-ending queue, with jobs waiting to be done. I also became more involved, as Technical Director, in a wide range of other ship design work, including hull structural design, vibration problems, engineering of all kinds, hydraulics, classification society rules and regulations, damaged stability, freeboard and loadline regulations, as well as weight and building cost estimates for new designs. Our staff grew in numbers, as the work came in, and I was also fortunate to secure a nice contract from Poland, for the design of a new class of stern trawlers which they hoped to build for Canadian and other owners. After a while, I realised that my partnership agreement left much to be desired, that I did not

The Naval Architect

have the necessary financial control to ensure that I would ever reap the benefits of all my hard work in the company, which by then was growing in stature and prestige.

I therefore decided to accept an offer to join the prestigious firm of naval architects in Montreal, called G.T.R. Campbell International. George Campbell, head of the company, started his career as a ship surveyor, and had the knack of engaging people with a sound technical training. He had built up the Montreal office at that time, in 1967/68, to a staff complement of around 50 or more, and was busy with design work on the "Freedom" class of cargo ships of that era, and others, which were then built in large numbers by the major Japanese shipbuilders, such as Ishikawajima-Harima Industries Co. Ltd. or (I.H.I.), as it is known. George and I came to an agreement that I would accept to be Vice President and Technical Director for an eighteen month period, after which I would start up my own company in Montreal. His intention was to move his headquarters to Japan, and this involved some pruning of the Montreal staff, which we did. I was fortunate indeed to actively participate with him in the early design of the new breed of bulk carriers named the "Fortunes", which followed the Freedoms, and some OBO designs of that period. These unique ship designs embody, in one vessel, the main characteristics of a single-deck bulk carrier and of a closed shelter-deck vessel. These features mainly consist of the upper wing tanks and wide cargo hatches of the single decker, combined with the 'tween deck layout of the closed shelter deck vessel. This original concept of two vessels in one hull, allowed grain cargoes to be loaded in full compliance with the 1960 SOLAS regulations, without the need to construct grain feeders or to erect grain shifting boards. The lower cargo holds and 'tween decks are self-trimming, even when the entire cargo consists of heavy grain with a stowage factor of

45 cubic feet per ton. These self-trimming features also apply to the carriage of iron ore, potash, bauxite, coal, phosphate rocks and many other types of free-flowing bulk cargoes. The width of the hatches on the main deck, as well as the 'tween deck, was approximately 50% of the ship's beam, and the tank top was specially stiffened, so that grabs can be employed for the carriage of heavy cargoes These vessels are provided with two long and two short cargo holds, and served by twin and single hatches respectively, closed by MacGregor single pull covers. This combination of long and short holds allows for more flex-ibility in the loading and discharging of general or bulk cargoes at various ports, especially when the lengths of product vary considerably. The depth of the 'tween deck and its strength were specially designed to permit the loading of a wide range of unitised cargoes, including standard 8ft. x 8 ft. containers. They also permitted the use of fork lift trucks and other wheeled or tracked vehicles. The whole of the 'tween deck construction is flush throughout, and both it and the tank top, were designed for the stowage of containers or vehicular cargo. There were many other design features of this new type of cargo vessel, which were built to replace the old, aging, Liberty type ships of that era, and special efforts were made to ensure that they could be serviced in ports throughout the world. The fact that there were nearly 100 Freedom ships built for the international market, is proof enough that they were a great success, as were the SD14 vessels of similar concept, designed in the U.K. I also learned a lot about the commercial side of ship design and construction, much of which is not learned in books.

We also secured some local design work in Quebec, which together with the flood of paper work that seemed to spew out from Japan on a daily basis, kept everyone on their toes. I also soon learned, when working with George, that there was no such thing as an eight-hour day in a ship design office, and although I was used to putting in very long hours at the N.P.L., found that working with him was very demanding. I did however come to respect his boundless energy and enthusiasm and hoped that some of it would one day rub off onto me, - I think that it has!

He was also very good to me when we parted. I bought my pick of the furniture at his Montreal office for only a very nominal 100 Canadian dollars, and still enjoy some of the desks, oak book cases, office stools, chairs and drawing tables from that purchase, even to this day. Some people say I was one of the few people to ever part company with George on good terms. Some deservedly did not, but I really appreciated the kick-start that he gave me, which got me going on my own, when CDD Marine Inc. started life between 1968 and 1969, with a Quebec charter. We are now, some 30 years afterwards, the only firm remaining of those original 1968 Montreal-based naval architects and marine engineers, still wholly owned by the founders, and still active in business, despite the dramatic reductions in shipbuilding activity in Canada, and elsewhere, which have occurred over the intervening years. Fortunately, I learned, early on, that survival in the marine industry necessitates the ability to adapt to change, and over the years from 1966 to the present time, there have certainly been plenty of those, and not only in Canada. Unlike some of our competitors in Montreal, now defunct, we chose not to rely solely on government business, nor on any one country, but rather to strive to build and preserve a reputation for our work *based on sound, impartial, scientific knowledge and technical expertise*. As subsequent events were to show, this policy, although not always the most lucrative, has proved to be the best for our clients, and thus ensured our continuing success. We also enjoy working with other consultants in the marine world, some of them in other countries, and have learned that sharing projects with them can be a very rewarding experience, good for all those concerned.

I commenced company operations on St. James' Street, Montreal, just opposite the C.I.B.C. bank building, as a firm of naval architects and marine engineers, with a staff of five, some of whom had followed me from G.T.R. Campbell International. We already had some small on-going projects, which I had secured with George, and these helped to get us "up and running". It was not easy, and I still wonder how we managed to survive those first few years so well, although I was very fortunate indeed to have a lot of close support from my special friends. We were also very fortunate that, about that time, there was a great need for expertise in several areas of marine research in which I had published papers whilst at the N.P.L. By what now seems to be incredibly good fortune, many of these marine requirements originated in the United States, and those seeking this expertise, managed to find me in Montreal. It is perhaps very fortunate that the marine industry is so closely knit, and that there is a kind of "bush telegraph" which operates throughout the world so that information can be gathered extraordinarily quickly, if not always accurately. I was therefore lucky enough that a firm specialising in marine propulsion systems needed some expertise in propeller design. We were approached by the firm, who were based in Seattle, Washington, U.S.A., to re-design twin screw propellers for a high speed ferry. This vessel was of the semi-planing type, and calculations showed that the original propellers would cavitate under load, mainly due to excessive thrust loading on the blades. We therefore re-designed the propellers with a smaller diameter, giving greater tip clearance from the hull surface, clear of the boundary layer, and therefore with less likelihood of propeller-induced vibration. In addition, the root stresses of the new propeller blades were also reduced, even though some reduction in the blade section thickness was made. Various other successful modifications were suggested, which reduced the actuation loads on the controllable pitch mechanism. This project became the fore-runner of many similar investigations conducted for that firm, and others made on behalf of several marine design firms of consultants in the United States, one of which involved the prediction by CDD of the full scale performance of two ferries, driven by gas turbines. Various configurations of patented marine drive systems were compared, and their corresponding full-scale speed performance estimated, using design methods I had developed at the N.P.L. The conclusions from this work were far reaching, since we found that were there large differences in speed performance between the three designs, so that not only could the best one be chosen, but there were also large losses in speed performance shown to apply to *each* design, on account of the effects of shallow water, windage on the superstructure, and increases in ship displacement. Since there were heavy financial penalties in the shipbuilding contract for losses in speed performance below the contract speed, it became very clear that all of these factors had to be taken into account when fixing the power requirements of these vessels, which had to operate in shallow water. I found out, years later, that our results were considered so important and of such economic consequence that they had been checked out by running an expensive series of shallow water tank tests in the U.K. I was also informed by a good friend who had worked at these test facilities, that the tank test results fully confirmed our predictions to a close order of accuracy. As is so often the case in marine matters, we were never told of those *confirmatory* tank test results, but no doubt would have heard, very quickly, in the alternative situation if they had differed significantly from our earlier predictions!

The Early Days of Expo '67 -and Beyond

One of our early local designs, which proved to be a very interesting concept, was a survey and inspection vessel built for the port of Montreal, named the MAISONNEUVE. Many important visitors to Montreal have been invited to sit at its magnificent dining table!. This design was rather unique at the time, since the propulsion drive was a single propeller working in a tunnel. I designed the hull in the form of Vee-shaped sections, with the tunnel cut out from the bottom of the Vee sections, just above the keel line at the after end. This was a design feature we had used before at the N.P.L., when we had been appointed to solve the problems of a Laker vessel which not only vibrated badly, but which had poor steering and manoeuvring characteristics. The original design was found to have too full a sectional shape at the after end of the vessel, *ahead of the propeller and rudder*. This over-filling of the stern sections, by the original designers, had resulted in a starvation of the water flow into the propeller and rudder, which led to its poor performance. The solution was to incorporate a special tunnel at the lower part of the stern, ahead of the propeller and rudder, which gave a dramatically improved flow of water into them, and thus cured the problem, at minimal cost to the owners. Ship designers do not sometimes appreciate that water will always vigorously protest, if you try to force it to turn through more than a certain angle, which you can only find out by experience, for each particular design. *The "school of experience" is one of the best places of learning to attend, but the entry fees are often found to be rather onerous!*

We prepared the design and working drawings, all to the approval of the client, the National Harbours Board of Montreal, and the rules and regulations of the Canada Shipping Act. We were also designated to prepare any additional working drawings required by the successful contractor, and to supervise the construction of the vessel. After preparing the design, specification, and working drawings, we were instructed to invite a number of smaller builders to bid on the design package. The successful builder was Fercraft Marine of Montreal, who did a first class job, working under our supervision. The owners of that company were the Daoust brothers, Fernand and Albert, and that is when I first met Raymond Daoust, the son of Fernand, now a well-known naval architect in Montreal with his own design company. Raymond and I have worked together from time to time over the years, and even appeared on the same *and* opposite sides of the court, in some marine cases which required expert opinion. I have a great respect for his attitude to hard work. Corporately, we were also fortunate to have both local design work and work from overseas organisations in several other countries, where we had commenced early marketing operations. These activities eventually extended to several South American countries, such as Columbia, Ecuador, Venezuala, Mexico, Chile and Peru, and in South East Asia to Malaysia, Singapore, Thailand and Burma, and even to such far away countries as Iran, India and Pakistan, all of which I had to visit on a fairly regular basis for several years, and still sometimes do! As we have found so many times, the services of a good Agent who is able to advise on local customs and practices, are fundamental requirements in meeting the needs of clients in these various countries, and in doing business on a sound basis.

CHAPTER VI

AS A MARINE CONSULTANT

I suppose that my continuing second career, as an **independent marine consultant**, started in 1968, in Montreal, with some help and encouragement from a few close friends. In retrospect, I sometimes wonder why so few of us have been able to survive the "ups and downs" of the marine industry, over the intervening 30 years since that time: it has not been easy. Most of those engaged in that period in similar marine consulting activities in Quebec, and other parts of Canada, seem to have either disappeared from the scene completely, or have been taken over by outside interests, thus losing their independence. This aspect of the marine business becomes very important when experts are to be selected for litigation or arbitration proceedings, since to find one with no visible, or even hidden connections, to either one of the parties to an action is often very difficult.(Ref.33) As far as design work is concerned, this has proved over the years to be too costly and time consuming for smaller companies to bid upon, unless they have the benefit of a directed contract from the client on account of their superior expertise, or they are compensated for their efforts when invited to make a competitive, preliminary, design proposal. Their design functions can vary considerably, depending on the nature and scope of the project, but can extend to any or each of the following:

1. Ship dimensions and preliminary power estimates
2. Preliminary lines and body plan of the vessel
3. Derived hydrostatic data, such as draft, trim, preliminary stability,

Bonjean* curves (* see nomenclature)

4. Freeboard and floodable lengths for compartmentation of the vessel
5. Hull and machinery lay-outs and how they can best be incorporated in the design
6. Hull structure- Strength and vibration of the ship
7. Detailed power requirements- Main Engines and auxiliaries
8. Lightship, weight estimates and centres of gravity
9. Compartment capacities, trim and intact stability
10. Damaged stability, Freeboard and Load line Regulations
11. Building cost estimates
12. Detail design- Working plans for ship fitting, welding, outfitting, machinery and equipment installation and control, pipe fitting and installation, system definition and installation.

To arrive at these various stages of the final design, many of the earlier design stages will need to be iterated, so that the development of the detailed contract working plans and a ship specification can be prepared. These will be used by the bidding shipyards to prepare offers for the construction of the ship, and used in contract negotiations with the accepted bidder. These design phases involve all engineering groups of the designer's team, and it is his final responsibility, as naval architect, to ensure that the ship will be completely defined by the contract plans and specification, so that the owner's operating requirements are respected in every detail. This final design can be prepared by the shipowner's own design team of naval architects, in order to obtain bids, or it may be a design prepared on their behalf by a marine consulting company, specialising in those particular ships. Many times also, the design can be an "in house" one prepared by a shipyard for the international market, and which perhaps, with some slight modifications, will meet a particular owner's requirements. This latter method can usually only be adopted when the design changes do not interfere with the original basic design concept, since if this is based on sound economic as well as technical principles, the profitability of the vessel should be assured to cover a wide range of operating variables. On this subject, we have often been requested to make *technical and economic studies* for specific ship classes, so that the selected design to be built will be near-optimal, even though the market forces change, as they inevitably do from time to time.

Studies of this type have proved to be invaluable for the optimisation of such ships as bulk carriers, deep sea and coastal tankers, passenger-cargo vessels, oil-bulk-ore carriers, ferries, fishing vessels of all kinds, fisheries training vessels, and many other specialised vessels where the income can be highly variable and where a down-turn in the market can have considerable economic effects on the ship operations. As an example of this philosophy, we were able to show, even back in 1979, that a *second-hand*, five years old, combination fishing vessel of around 47 metres in length (155 feet), gave a clear economic advantage over a new vessel of the same size and otherwise equal characteristics. These improvements in profitability for the older vessel were maintained also over a wide range of variations in fish prices from year to year, variable costs of repairs and maintenance of the hull and machinery, replacement of the fishing gear, including nets and bobbins, and other variables, all of which were reflected in the net present value (N.P.V.) of the respective vessels. We also made similar analyses for two factory-type fishing trawlers, one new and the other 8 years old, both able to process and freeze their catches on board. Again, in this case, even after allowing for quite major technical upgrading of the older vessel, there was only a minor economic advantage in favour of the new vessel. Some Owners might therefore prefer choosing the less expensive, second-hand vessel, with the shorter life, and leave themselves the option of getting back their invested capital in only 9 years, compared with 17 years for the new vessel. Another analysis was made for tuna seiners catching yellow fin and skipjack back in 1974. This showed that such vessels below 1,100 tons fish hold capacity could not recover the total costs of production per ton of fish landed, and they were therefore considered to be unprofitable. This analysis was extended in 1979 and showed that even larger vessels up to 1,800 tons capacity were then getting to be uneconomical, and that only the larger, vertically integrated, fishing organisations could run their operations and make a small profit margin, justified only by their ability to make additional profits on the distribution, processing and sales of canned tuna, and their by-products such as pet foods and fertiliser. A classic "break-even" cost analysis of Canadian East Coast fishing vessels was made in 1977, including long liners, stern draggers, scallop vessels and lobster boats. We showed that the largest 155 foot stern trawlers were the only class not to achieve the break-even fish price required. The smaller vessels were shown to be more cost efficient at that time, especially the long-liners and scallop draggers. **Subsequent world-wide events in the fishing industry have now confirmed how its future decline could have been predicted, using the results of such techno-economic analyses.** Perhaps the same methods can be applied to its recovery.

In September, 1981 I received a personal call from Tom Bender, President of Bender Shipyards, Mobile, Alabama. They were within a few weeks of side launching a large fishing vessel for Mexican interests, and had apparently been successfully using my papers on sideways launching for several years, in order to achieve a safe launch at their facilities.(Refs. 3, 4) How they found me was quite interesting, since my papers on sideways launching, written whilst I was working at the N.P.L., were dated around 1955, and in 1981 they had no idea whether the author of those papers, was alive, dead or just not around! By sheer coincidence, it transpired that John Logan, a marine Sales Manager from Seattle, Washington, was visiting the firm, and whilst passing by a group of technical people in the shipyyard, he heard that they were looking for someone with my name, who could perhaps help them with an opinion on their up-coming launch. He knew me by name, and that I was practising in Montreal, from which they were able to track me down via Vancouver, to my offices on St. James' Street. I then received the phone call from Mr. Tom Bender, who requested me to send him an opinion on their forthcoming launch. After reviewing the launch data for the vessel, which they gave me, I sent him a fax which indicated that the launch was likely to prove rather difficult and that unless certain changes were made, a large outward angle of roll could be expected, as the vessel was "fitted-out" to a large extent with a high centre of gravity. I was then mandated to go to their yard in Mobile, Alabama, to see the launch site at first hand, and to make recommendations on the launch procedure. It was a most interesting assignment. The best solution within the time available, was to attach restraining wires to the top-sides of the vessel, and to restrict the angle of outward roll, by attaching them to large concrete blocks which acted as drags on the vessel whilst it was on the ways and also when rolling out and away from the quay edge.(see Figure 17) Calculations were made of the way-end velocities, the bearing pressures on the ways, the static drop, the outward and inward angles of roll on impact, and several other parameters which affected the sideways launch of this vessel, which was a large tuna-seiner. Three restraining wires were attached to the bulwarks of the vessel, and these were calculated to be able to reduce the outward roll to about 30 degrees. There was some concern as to the process however,

Figure 17   Photograph of a sideways launch.

Courtesy of Bender Shipyards Mobile, Alabama.

since there were already two other similar vessels higher up the launching ways, and the restraining wires had to pass underneath them, during the launching operation. This meant that there was a possibility that the concrete blocks might snag on the other vessels as they passed under them, and bring them crashing down on the vessel being launched. The shipyard personnel did a first class job in making all the preparations for the launch, according to my recommendations, making the blocks, lining up their run, and securing them to the ship's bulwarks. On the day of the launch there was a large crowd of onlookers, including some visiting dignatories from Washington and Mexico, all of whom seemed to sense the impending drama, as the large tuna seiner started its descent down the ways. Figure 17 shows a sister vessel at its maximum angle of outward roll, and the large wave generated. All went according to plan, and there were no damages to the vessel, either on impact or on the return roll towards the quay edge. I still remember Tom Bender striding towards me and making some nice congratulatory comments, as the vessel hit the water, and I emerged from under the launch ways in the centre of the site. The splendid Bender Shipyard crew, who had worked with me to put everything in order for the launch, kindly invited me to their own celebrations, after the launch was successfully completed. From a commercial point of view, the successful launch of such a vessel in a nearly completed state of building, was obviously of economic importance for expanding operations in the yard, and pointed the way to the future. I therefore suggested, before leaving Mobile to go back to Canada, that the yard could perhaps take benefit from a patented launching device which we had developed in CDD Marine, for that purpose, and known as the Hiley Brake System. I had originally worked with my old friend Alfred Hiley, who I have already mentioned, in developing this launch system in England. It consists of a series of compression blocks anchored to foundations on the launch site, through which twin steel wire ropes (SWR's), are passed under compression during the launch. The free-ends of these steel wire ropes are attached to the shoreside bulwarks of the vessel to be launched. The SWR's are then set to a pre-calculated value of tension, by tightening up the compression blocks, such that when the vessel starts its outward rotation at the way ends, they restrain the outward angle of roll and keep it within safe limits, otherwise the vessel might capsize in certain circumstances. An Agreement was eventually concluded with the shipyard, whereby we supplied them with a design package to enable the Hiley Brakes to be manufactured at their facilities, under licence. We later received a series of photographs from the builders, showing a sister ship of the original tuna vessel being successfully launched with our new Hiley Brake System. As shown in Figure 17, the vessel is at its maximum outward angle of roll from the edge of the quay, and the restraining wires attached to the port side bulwarks are clearly visible under tension and acting as designed to restrict the roll angle.

On one memorable occasion back in the eighties, I went with a group of other experts from Canada on an evaluation mission to Mexico, to explore the potential for investing in new fishing projects in that country. We were well received by the various government agencies and commercial interests concerned, and were on our way back to the airport when my local agent suggested that we still had time to call in en route at the Department of Fisheries. We were well received, even at such short notice, by the Deputy Minister who was a naval architect by training, having studied at Southampton University, in England. He was very eloquent and described how he had returned to his home country, after graduating and working in some shipyards in the south of England. He then referred to a ship design method he had used very successfully whilst in the U.K., and which he had continued to use whilst developing the Mexican fishing fleets in his country. He also described how he had once won the building contract for a new ship, by using this method to achieve the owners required ship speed. He had been able to propose a smaller engine than usually required for this type of vessel, which the method indicated to be possible with its suggested optimum hull form. Having won the contract over many other competitors, mainly on account of the smaller engine, optimum hull form, and reduced building costs, he then built and delivered the ship accordingly. He was delighted to state that all his expectations had been achieved, the owner was very pleased, and the heavy speed penalties which would have applied in the event of not meeting the contract speed, were not invoked. At this point, my agent became very excited, and I sensed from my rather limited Spanish, that the method the Deputy Minister had been talking about was the design method on optimised trawler forms, which I had presented to the F.A.O. in Rome, in 1959. (see Refs.19 to 23) The Minister, when informed that the author of the design papers he had been using so successfully over the years, was in fact standing next to him in the same room, became very excited and then broke open a bottle to mark the occasion.

We departed for the airport at Mexico City, in good spirits, just in time to catch the plane. I remember thinking afterwards that I could have easily ended my days, never knowing that my work was being put to such good use by a naval architect from another country, and how our paths had fortunately crossed for a brief, but happy moment in time. I have since been informed that this design method still forms part of the curriculum at many Universities, in those countries with maritime interests, that teach naval architecture.

Portugal is one of those maritime countries, which has gone through many political and economic changes in the last 25 years or so, and I was indeed very fortunate to have seen most of them. I have been going to Portugal from the age of ten, and soon became endeared with the charm of its people, its customs, cuisine, and way of life, although to some it may appear rather complicated and perhaps difficult to understand. It helps if you are a family person! I met several notables from the old "families" who in the days under Salizar ran the whole country, and was fortunate to be engaged by some of them on several projects for their overseas fisheries sector. Fishing was of course, and still is, a vital part of the Portuguese economy and their way of life. I was busy working on several such fisheries projects, when their October revolution came along, which I witnessed at first hand in Estoril, outside Lisbon. It was a quiet affair, no bloody clashes in the streets, and almost overnight the people were in charge after several generations of dictatorship. Of course this meant a disruption of many ongoing projects, and there were several cases where we met outright resistance to change, and even in one case, suspected sabotage of a vessel which we had converted to a new system of freezing, which required an armed guard to be posted on board. This patented system was eventually taken up by Japanese interests and used for the deep freezing of tuna and similar species which are highly prized when freshly caught, and then frozen down to -60 degrees Celsius, vacuum-packed, and later thawed in a nearly "as caught" perfect condition. Despite all the political upheaval of that time, and social unrest in the transitional period before full democracy arrived, we were able to continue working from Canada for the new régime, with several new designs of deep sea trawlers, tuna vessels, shrimp and lobster vessels, some in steel and others in fibre glass, for Portuguese commercial interests. Most of these projects were under the direction of the Portuguese Committee for Fisheries Development, in Lisbon, which represented the interests of the fishing industry at that time. Stern trawlers, for example, were designed to operate from South African ports such as Mossamedes, which were within easy range of abundant fishing grounds, particularly for species such as hake, which is highly prized for its size and taste by many countries that border the Southern Atlantic ocean. The design was based on freezing of the catch, returning to the home port with a full catch in about 40 days, and trans-shipment of the frozen fish back to Portugal by reefer. We made a techno-economic computer study of the whole operation, which was shown to be very profitable. Unfortunately, just when the project was about to be implemented, Angola, or Portuguese West Africa, as it used to be known, decided to go its own way and become independent. The war in Angola decided the fate of many similar projects which were in the planning stages in Portugal at that time, and which of course were never funded, because of the political and economic uncertainty which such violence brings in its wake. **A great pity that the lessons of history are so seldom learned by succeeding generations.** Due to the upheaval created by the war in Angola, several owners then turned to their domestic fleets for conversion of some existing vessels to more efficient freezing methods, and improved fishing gear. Others were interested in developing new markets for export of fishing vessels, and other craft which could utilise the new marine materials coming on the market at that time. One of the many projects undertaken for Portuguese owners was the conversion of some 55 metre, cod fishing vessels, which traditionally made the long trip to the Grand Banks off Newfoundland. The design drawings and complete specifications were prepared for conversion of these vessels to mid-water trawlers, complete with refrigeration for freezing the catches, so that they were able to fish for longer periods, without spoilage of the fish. Several other similar design projects were also completed for Portuguese owners at that time.

One of the new materials then coming into increasing favour for fishing vessels in the early seventies, was fibreglass reinforced plastics, known as F.R.P. in North America, and sometimes as G.R.P. or glass reinforced plastics in some parts of Europe. F.R.P, or G.R.P., are high performance structural laminates which are very strong in relation to their weight, and which in combination with some other materials, such as wood, can be used very effectively in integral structural design. These laminates are essentially combinations of high strength glass fibres, bonded with resins of much lower strength, which can be used to form section shapes and hull surfaces suitable for the construction of fishing vessels, yachts, and pleasure craft of all kinds. Fibreglass filaments, usually less than one thousandth of an inch in diameter, are manufactured in parallel bundles or "strands", which are used in turn to make several different kinds of construction material. These consist of roving, the most common and economical form of these materials, cloth and woven roving, chopped strand mat, and cut strands. Each form of the F.R.P. material has a specific structural quality, which can be used by the designer to arrive at the most efficient hull for any particular application. For example, rovings which are unidirectional, parallel elements, used for reinforcement, can be woven into heavy coarse fabric, chopped into strands for use in forms and mats, or sprayed for direct application onto a mould. Woven roving on the other hand, generally consists of flattened bundles or rovings which form a square pattern. Different weave patterns may be obtained for specific applications, ranging in weight from 15 to 30 ounces per square yard. Cloths are woven from twisted and plied strands of glass filaments, and various weaves, including plain, satin and unidirectional, are commercially available in a wide variety of weights. We prepared a complete design package for some 32 metre shrimp and sardine vessels, suitable for F.R.P. construction in Portugal, which included hull, machinery and electrical specifications and also made recommendations for their domestic manufacture. These were influenced to some extent by a study we had undertaken for the Department of Industry Trade and Commerce, of the Quebec Government, also made for the purpose of setting up F.R.P. facilities for the manufacture of commercial fishing vessels in Quebec. Many Quebec companies successfully took up this technology later, for commercial fishing vessel construction, as well as for luxury yachts. The study involved making field trips to the United States, which was at that time one of the leaders in the design and building of vessels in fibreglass reinforced plastics, especially for large yachts and commercial fishing vessels of all kinds. (Ref.38) Visits were made to several facilities which manufacture yachts and commercial fishing vessels in the United States. Opportunity was also provided during the visits for us to compare production and building costs of traditional shrimp and lobster vessels, built in wood and steel, with new vessels built in F.R.P., and also to interview several of their owners who were actively fishing the Eastern Seaboard and Southern Coast of the United States. All of the owners interviewed expressed their complete satisfaction with the F.R.P. construction of their vessels, and considered them to be excellent performers, even in heavy 10 foot seas in the Gulf of Mexico, when older, wooden vessels had to stop fishing. This was mainly on account of their lower bridge front and reduced superstructure height, which allowed more waves to come on board. I also noticed that these older *wooden* shrimp vessels showed signs of cracking of the hulls in the areas around the winch, the "A" frames for towing the two nets port and starboard, the deck connections, hawse pipes, freeing ports and around the hatchways. All of these areas on the F.R.P. vessels which we inspected, were in good condition, with no signs of cracking or deformation of the material. The main criticisms of these early U.S. designs, however, was that the selections for the auxiliary equipment and fishing gear had not been the best, nor made by marine consultants with experience in the fishing industry. Many owners had found it necessary, for example, to make modifications to the location, size and type of the fishing gear, before they could commence their fishing operations. This led to costly delays before some of them could start their fishing operations. Other owners had also found it necessary to make changes to improve the layout of the engine room, and increased the size of the cooling fans, fitted more accessible and trouble-free bilge piping system, re-located the fuel lines in the engine room, fitted a boom and tackle over the main engine for engine overhaul, cut a hatch in the bridge deck to provide direct overhead access to the main engine, for easier repairs and maintenance, and fitted better noise insulating material under the deck head of the wheelhouse, to reduce noise levels in that vicinity. All of these changes would have been anticipated by competent naval architects, with specialised expertise of the fishing industry.

Probably the first F.R.P. trawler to be built on production lines in the United States, was the "R.C.Brent, Jr.", which was initiated by Newport Fiberglass Trawlers, Inc. in Newport, Florida, in 1967. This vessel was made in fibreglass reinforced plastics, from the mould of an existing trawler, built in ferro-cement. The main hull was of sandwich construction, with double 3/4 inch end grain balsa core throughout. The F.R.P. skins consisted of alternate layers of 1.5 ounces per square foot mat and 24 ounces per square yard woven roving, as already defined earlier. The bottom of the hull was reinforced with wood floors wrapped in F.R.P., and the deck was made in wood covered with F.R.P. This early type of hull construction has since been superseded in many ways, although even at that time, it proved to be very robust, much lighter than steel or wood, more durable in service conditions, and with reduced maintenance costs. Not long after the "R.C.Brent Jr." came into service, the original company split into two new companies, one called Modern Fiber Glass Inc., based in Tampa, Florida, and the other Advanced Fiberglass Shipbuilders Inc. of Tallahassee, Florida. The first company was a division of Ashland Oil Co. which continued with production of the 72 footers from the mould of the original vessel, whilst the second company developed a new 86 foot trawler which was first launched in 1970, only being superseded in length when a new series of 93 foot vessels were built in Peru about that time. The first of the Tampa built trawlers was the "Charlie", which was later expanded into a new line of 80 footers, designed in co-operation with Gibbs & Cox, Inc. of New York, who are specialized in this type of construction for commercial vessels and pleasure craft. Hatteras Yacht Division of North American Rockwell Corp. one of the facilities which we visited at New Bern, North Carolina, as part of our study for the Quebec Government, had also expanded their very popular line of large pleasure yachts to include the production of shrimp trawlers at that time. These 74 foot F.R.P. shrimp trawlers, of which 12 were built about that time, were those which we had visited earlier in our tour and discussed with their owners. (Ref. 38) Desco Marine Inc., a division of Whittaker Corp. located at St. Augustine, Florida, the largest builder of shrimp trawlers in the world at that time, started the production of their first F.R.P. vessel in 1970. Prior to this time they were specialized in wood construction, which was then the material of choice of many fishing countries, on account of its availability, and general worldwide acceptance as the traditional material for boatbuilding. Fibreglass fishing vessels built around the early 1970's did not utilise their full potential for structural weight reductions, compared with wood or steel. This was mainly on account of the extensive use of wood integrated into their construction, a conservative, traditional attitude towards a new material, and the fact that the fuel tanks were required by regulation to be made of steel and not integrated into the design of the main hull. The net result on fishing vessels built at that time was that for a typical 75-80 foot vessel, the actual savings in hull weight of one built in F.R.P. compared to one built of steel or wood, were only 20 to 25%, compared with a potential improvement of at least 50%, on theoretical grounds. Again, due to adherence to many old traditional forms of hull shape for the shrimp trawlers, many of the design advantages available in F.R.P. construction were not immediately realised. This fact often introduced unnecessary problems into the design of F.R.P. vessels, since discontinuities in the hull surface, such as at the bilges, create regions of high stress in the F.R.P. which would not otherwise have been present, if the surfaces were fair. Probably the most difficult aspects of design of fishing vessels in F.R.P. are the *connections* between the hull and the deck, at the bulwarks, and the foundations required for high stress areas such as winches, the mast, and boom supports. All of these connections are subjected to high stress levels and potential impact damages in service conditions, with consequent possibility of "racking" of the structure. Racking, the tendency for two connecting structural members to change their relative positions at their point of intersection, is caused by fluctuating wave forces. These regularly impact the sides and bottom of any vessel in a seaway, and in turn produce high local stresses in the connecting material. If these stresses are high enough, and of sufficient duration, they will eventually result in fracture at the joints where the connections were made. Experience has shown that the best connections should be a combination of fibreglass sheathing and local reinforcements. These can be either of wood or metallic material, and should be integrated into the main hull to spread any impact or flexing loads over as wide an area as possible. Other structural problems in F.R.P. construction, which have been solved in several different ways, are those which involve the lining of the fish holds, deckhouse attachments to the deck, engine foundations for winches and generators, attachments for the stern tubes and propeller bearings, the rudders, and pintle supports.

Glass reinforced plastics, (G.R.P.), as a structural material for naval patrol and surveillance vessels, has been in increasing demand since the the mid 1950's, and several countries were involved in that early development work, mainly in Europe. In the U.K., under the sponsorship of research programs funded by the Admiralty at that time, several prototype naval craft were built in G.R.P. One of the first of these for deep, sea-going application, was a minesweeper of 150 feet in length, (46 metres), constructed in 1971 by Vosper Thornycroft Limited, at their Southampton Shipyard, Hampshire, U.K. Other well known companies in the U.K. specialised in G.R.P. construction from that time such as Halmatic Limited, and Fairey Marine, have also made concentrated efforts into the design and construction of work boats, crew boats, yachts, shallow draft, rescue and medical service boats, and other forms of high speed craft for domestic and overseas markets. (Ref.39)

Since G.R.P. is non-magnetic and transparent to radar, it has also found wide aceptance in naval circles where these qualities are of prime importance. For example, fast patrol boats and surveillance type vessels, where detection avoidance is required, can benefit from the radar transparency qualities of the material. Since the speeds of such planing craft are also very sensitive to changes in displacement, weight savings in fibreglass hulls, compared with aluminum and wood, often result in improved ship speeds for the same installed horse power. Alternatively, where economy may sometimes be more important, the resulting weight savings can be used to reduce the required engine horse power and yet still maintain the same top speed. In the last few years, there have been several further advances in the development of new materials for small to medium size ship applications. These new materials, often in composite form, have influenced the design and construction of high speed vessels such as passenger and car ferries, patrol craft, multi-hull vessels such as catamarans, trimarans, hovercraft and similar SES vehicles, whilst some of them have also made their way into military applications. The classification societies such as Lloyd's Register of Shipping, the American Bureau of Ships, Det Norske Veritas, Bureau Veritas and other such leading bodies have kept pace with these latest developments, and formulated new rules for the approval of such marine craft, built in these new composite materials. For example, a composite built vessel might consist of combination of high tensile "E" fibreglass, mat and PVC for the main hull, Kevlar 49 for the superstructure and carbon for such items as rudders and other external appendages, where stiffness is important. Looking back over the last 40 years of marine development, particularly in high speed craft, it is apparent that there has been a continual improvement in vessel performance over a wide front, much of which derives from these developments in material design.

Probably the most disappointing material for marine application has proved to be ferro-cement, which compared with steel, aluminum, wood, and fibreglass has not found the general acceptance which back in the 1970's seemed to be possible for use in the construction of fishing vessels, work boats, yachts and similar craft. These vessels have been built over the years in countries such as Canada and the U.S.A., Britain, New Zealand, Egypt, Fiji, Jamaica, Dahomey, Hong Kong and Thailand,

and especially in those countries which lack traditional boat building materials. Popularity of this method of construction has come mainly from amateur boat builders, who were interested in acquiring a new, custom-made vessel, and who had the patience and tenacity required to learn the techniques, and assemble the work force and materials necessary to cement and plaster up the hull. The sequence of main events typically required to build a vessel about 75 feet in length, in ferro-cement, consists of the following:

- **Make a well connected, faired surface, armature of welded pipe construction and longitudinal rods, covered with sheets of square wire mesh. Welded pipes (3/4") diameter, are used to form the frame of the armature, to which 1/4" longitudinals and frames are attached, and then set up on the pipe keel.**
- **Plaster all the meshed surface from both sides. For the main hull, start from the inside and work outwards.**
- **Scrape and brush the excess plaster from the vertical, horizontal, and inside and outside surfaces of the main hull.**
- **Fair the outer surface of the hull**
- **Cure the hull by running water over the hull surfaces**
- **After curing, usually up to 28 days, coat the outer surface with a glazing compound. Faster, steam curing, is sometimes used**
- **When the outer surface is set, sand and shape to final dimensions and smoothness**

The plastering operation is the most demanding, since it must be completed in two or three hours, without any deformation of the armature whilst applying the mortar to the meshed surfaces. A team of professional plasterers will obviously do the best job, since the work is very intensive for a comparatively short time, and amateurs can easily tire on the job. They can however assist in the early stages of the work on the keel, which requires a relatively high volume of mortar to encapsulate the reinforcing rods, running longitudinally inside the keel. The composition of the mortar mix during the plastering operation is obviously one which requires careful control, and classification society rules require that test samples be taken throughout the plastering stage. To ensure continuity of the mix and full penetration of the plaster around the reinforcements, a vibrator is employed, which helps to eliminate any air pockets or void spaces around the rods and mesh in the keel. The next stage of plastering is the main hull, working from the inside of the hull to form the inner surface, pushing the mix through the meshes, and then forming the "scratch" surface from the outside. This scratch surface is faired and smoothed as much as possible, and then left to harden a little, before final fairing, in preparation for application of the final coat. This final "skin" coat determines the asthetics and fairness of the completed vessel, and is usually between 1/16" to 1/8" inch in thickness above the surface of the outer mesh. The third surface to plaster up is the main deck and any other horizontal surfaces. In order to make a complete penetration of these surfaces, it is usual to work with a peg board on the underside of the deck, so that the plaster can be applied from above to form the upper surface, and then vibrated through the mesh to make a complete bond, without dropping out. Plaster is then applied from underneath, to form the under surface of the deck. Vertical surfaces such as tanks and frames are usually plastered at the same time as the decks. The second grade work, which can again be done by amateurs, consists of scraping and brushing off all loose mortar inside the hull, on surfaces such as decks, bulkheads, inner shell, tank boundaries, web frames and top of the keel. The choice of materials for the cement mix is very much a question of knowledge and experience of local conditions, since ambient temperature can play a large part in the setting and curing of the hull. Type V Portland cement seems to be favoured in the Northern hemisphere, mixed with clean, sharp, fine sand which has been well washed before mixing. Some builders prefer to use additives such as pozzolan to improve the working properties of the mix, and others also use bonding agents made of latex or epoxy resins, to bond special areas where good connections are required in way of fittings and attachments to the hull. Since cement mixes only harden through hydration, it is necessary to *water cure* the hull in order to obtain the proper compressive strength. Water is therefore run continuously over the concrete surfaces, for a period of about 28 days, and at the end of that time the hull will have achieved about 95% of its full compressive strength. Some commercial builders have used steam curing to accelerate the hardening process, thereby drastically reducing the time required before moving the hull for outfitting work. Although ferro-cement has therefore found some favour as a shipbuilding material for some smaller vessels, it has not had the commercial success of other contending materials such as steel, aluminum, wood and fibreglass. This is mainly on account of its greater vulnerability to impact and shock damage, its lack of transverse strength in shear, a tendency to crack under oscillating loads, brittleness and poor freeze/thaw characteristics, and the fact that it is permeable. Water is therefore able to migrate through the mass of the material in response to changes in humidity, unless the wetted surfaces are specially treated to withstand water absorption.

Aluminum, as an alternative shipbuilding material to steel, has proved to be much more readily accepted in the industry, than ferro-cement. There are many reasons for this, the most significant being that it has only 1/3 the weight of steel. It is therefore most valuable as a shipbuilding material when the applications are such that savings in weight result directly in speed improvements, which of course is the case for fast patrol craft, search and rescue operations, work boats, ferries and similar craft which have to run on a schedule. Due to its high strength, the strength/weight ratios of the strongest aluminum alloys are superior to most other isotropic materials used in shipbuilding. It has other advantages for some military uses, since it is non-magnetic, although with good electrical conductivity. Due to the extensive searches for potential marine applications, which have been investigated by the aluminum industry over the years, the qualities which are most important for fabrication and long life have been well defined. These include the ease of joining, weldability, corrosion control, extrusion and surface preparation. Since the elastic modulus of aluminum is also only 1/3 that of steel, stresses due to impact, badly fitting joints and misalignments are low. (Ref. 40) The coefficient of linear expansion of aluminum is twice that of steel, which means that although thermal stresses are lower than steel, care must be taken when joining materials, such as occurs at the intersection of steel decks with aluminum superstructures. This difference in expansion has been the cause of some structural problems in the past, although these are now better understood, and unlikely to be recurrent. The ease of manufacture of aluminum facilitates the extrusion process, and there is therefore a wide range of section shapes available, which make for easy assembly, design and structural efficiency, and a good workmanlike appearance. Although structural aluminum is also not subject to brittle fracture at low temperature, it requires special design consideration at temperatures beyond 93 degrees Celsius. It has, however, been used successfully in the industry, with careful design, up to 260 degrees Celsius. Aluminum also has another important property for marine use, which is that it has a strong resistance to corrosive attack, due to the formation of aluminum oxide on its unpainted surfaces. The corrosion layer formed on the surface of the bare aluminum is non-toxic and colourless, which makes it an ideal material for chemical or food applications on board ships. Aluminum also comes in many different forms, such as sheet, coil, plate, tubing, and pipe, as well as a variety of structural shapes in the form of extrusions and bars. Several of these structural forms have found a special place in the design and construction of ships, as well as the other smaller vessels we have discussed. One of the first aluminum alloys used in ship construction for superstructures, and for main hulls of smaller vessels up to about 30 metres in length, was Alcan #5083. This comes in the form of sheet and plate, and was the highest strength, non-heat-treatable alloy in general commercial use when it was introduced, back in the 1960's. It offers good welding and forming characteristics, excellent resistance to corrosion, and the same economy as in other non-heat-treatable alloys. It also has greater tensile strength in the annealed or welded condition, than some other types of aluminum alloys. Alcan #5086 on the other hand, is a medium strength alloy with excellent mechanical properties, a superior formability than #5083, and with excellent welding and corrosion resistance qualities. It is mainly used where its medium strength and good corrosion resistance qualities are required, such as tanks and cryogenic equipment, but is not recommended for corrosive environments above 60 degrees Celsius. Alloy 6351, by contrast, is widely used for structural shapes which are exposed to a corrosive environment and which also require good mechanical properties, and has found such applications in ship construction.

The welding of aluminum depends on two main techniques, the TIG and the MIG processes.

The TIG process (Tungsten Inert Gas), the first method developed for welding aluminum with an inert gas shield, is an arc welding process which uses a *non-consumable tungsten electrode* with either AC or DC current. Prior to that time, arc welding of aluminum had been mainly restricted to using a *consumable*, flux-coated electrode, which can create corrosion problems if the flux is not adequately removed. If the TIG process uses DC current, the electrode may be chosen positive (EP) or negative (EN), the latter being more suitable for the heavier plate gauges beyond 6.3 mm. and up to 25.4 mm. (i.e. between 1/4 and 1.0 inch). If the process uses AC current, the arc struck between the end of the tungsten electrode and the aluminum to be joined, can be adjusted for balance in polarity, which in turn controls the power penetration of the arc and its self-cleaning ability. Tungsten is chosen for the electrode because of its high melting point, and because it is a good source of electron emission. The inert gas, usually argon, shields the electrode and the molten weld metal from the effects of the atmosphere during the welding process, otherwise a film of aluminum oxide would form on the surface of the metal being melted, and inhibit the welding process. In general, TIG-(AC) is mainly used for manual welding and TIG-(DC) for automatic welding. Figure 19, reproduced by courtsey of The Aluminum Association Inc., shows the arrangement of the various components of the manual TIG process, including the welding machine, gas supply, tungsten electrode and holder, and the work. Welding can take place with or without filler metal added to the weld pool. In the former case, shown in Figure 19, the operator is required to use one hand for the filler and the other for the electrode, which requires a lot of dexterity and skill to make a good weld. Filler rod is usually 36 inches in length (914 mm.) and varies in diameter from 1/16 to 1/4 inches (1.6 to 6.3 mm.). If the TIG process is to be performed without filler metal, it is known as *autogenous* welding. Autogenous welding is mostly used for edge and corner welds, and also for automatic butt welding of light gauge sheet, but it is limited to alloys which are not prone to hot cracking

SCHEMATIC DIAGRAM OF THE TIG PROCESS

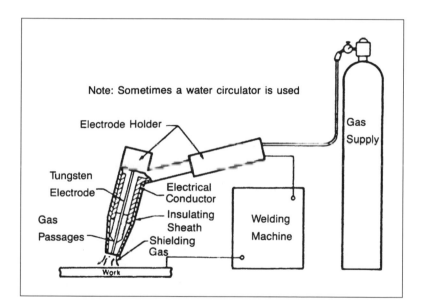

Figure 19   Schematic Diagram of the TIG process.

Courtesy of The Aluminum Association Inc. Washington, D.C. USA.

when the process is completed. For the automatic TIG-(DC) machine welding of aluminum, it is necessary to have a supply of cooling water for the gas torch head, and it is also usual to use helium for the shielding gas, which permits a higher arc temperature than for argon. The filler metal used in the automatic TIG-(DC) process is usually spooled wire, which is machine fed continuously and automatically to the weld pool.

The machine MIG (Metal Inert Gas) process which operates only on *direct current*, is used whenever the work to be welded can be fixed in a flat or horizontal position. The process is an arc welding method, which uses an aluminum or aluminum alloy wire as a *combined electrode and filler metal* in a direct current, electrode positive (DC-EP) arc and an inert shielding gas. Since the filler metal is added automatically to the weld pool, autogenous welding is not possible with the MIG process. The cost of setting up and operating machine MIG equipment must be justified by the extent of welding to be done. The MIG process can be either semi-automatic or fully automatic in operation, the former being preferred whenever quick changes in work position or direction are required, such as the butt welding of pipes. In the MIG process, the positive terminal of the power source is connected to the welding torch, and hence the electrode, whilst the negative terminal is connected to the work. An electric arc is therefore established between the *consumable aluminum wire electrode* and the work, both being in an inert gas shield, usually argon, that protects the weld pool from atmospheric contamination. The heat from the arc melts the end of the electrode and the adjacent parent metal, within the gas shield, such that small molten droplets of filler alloy are projected into the weld pool, where they solidify to become the weld metal at the welded joint. For the larger thicknesses of work, it is necessary to cool the torch by supplying a continuous flow of water to the torch head, as shown in Figure 20 by courtesy of The

SCHEMATIC DIAGRAM OF THE SEMI-AUTOMATIC MIG PROCESS

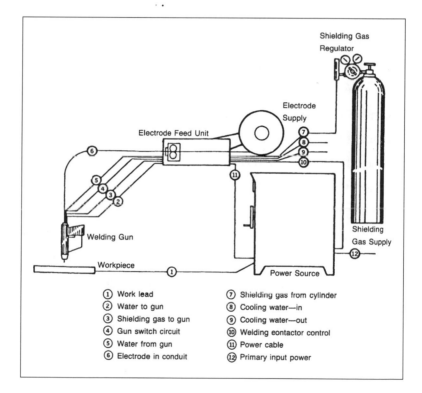

Figure 20   Schematic Diagram of the MIG process.

Courtesy of The Aluminum Association Inc. Washington, D.C. USA.

Aluminum Association Inc. Figure 20 also shows how the consumable electrode is machine fed into the welding gun at the workpiece, the cooling water supply in and out of the gun, and how the welding at the workpiece takes place with a supply of inert gas, fed into the gun. The MIG process therefore has several advantages over the TIG process, since there is no need for a flux, little spatter of the weld metal, the ability to weld in all positions, and an arc which removes the tough oxide film from the weld and thus facilitates joining of metal joints. Additional advantages of the MIG process over the TIG process, are that greater depths of weld penetration are possible, higher welding speeds can be achieved, and heat can be concentrated in smaller heat zones adjacent to the work, so that the MIG process is generally to be preferred. Both TIG and MIG welding methods rely on a well defined system of joint preparation and geometry, in order to ensure a successful aluminum weld. Factors which affect the choice of joint geometry include the thickness of the metal to be joined, whether backing plates are to be used and what type, the position of the point of application of the weld metal, and whether the welding is to be performed from one side or the other, or both. All of these factors affect the welding procedure, which in turn governs the extent of the weld penetration required, the weld bead shape and the welding speed, and these are usually specified by the designer and conform to certain accepted standards, such as the ANSI/AWS D1.2 (Structural Code-Aluminum) welding codes.

Steel, in many forms, is still the main material used in ship construction, particularly for the larger ships. It replaced wood and iron, which were the original traditional materials used in the shipbuilding industry up to the latter part of the last century. With the change from riveting to welding, which started in World War 2, and the more recent development of new materials for ship construction, radical changes in ship design have occurred, notably in the development of container ships, high speed passenger and car ferries, liquified gas carriers, offshore supply structures and several other novel, multi-hull ship types. In the tanker and chemical tanker classes, potential environmental problems have necessitated the change over from single to double hull construction, which in turn has required special design considerations for the avoidance of fatigue, corrosion, and brittle facture, especially at low temperatures. The development of new steel alloys, having improved strength to weight ratios and other desirable properties, has therefore been spurred on by the increased demand for these special ship types, and this is particularly so in the case of the new, much larger, passenger cruise ships. These vessels often cruise in wide temperature extremes, from cold Northern waters to much warmer Southern climates, and have many more open deck spaces for passenger recreation, which in turn have to be well supported and integrated into the main hull structure. Both of these requirements necessitate special alloys to cope with large temperature variations, and to withstand the impactive forces which occur on these enlarged passenger and work spaces. The older, ordinary strength steels used in ship construction are mainly plain carbon steels, with limits placed on the other components of the mix such as manganese, phosphorus, sulphur and silicon. These limits determine the grade of the steel produced, which can be made in open hearth, basic oxygen or electric furnaces, depending on the facilities of the steel manu-facturer. Higher strength steels, used in certain ship applications, have other special extra components in the mix, such as aluminum, columbium, manganese, nickel, vanadium and others, which promote micro-structural changes and thereby give improved strength. With these additions to the mix, and special heat treatment during the steel making process, yield strengths of steel up to 100,000 pounds per square inch (690 MPa), can be produced. Yield strengths for ordinary carbon steels are around 34,000 pounds per square inch, (235 MPa), whilst those for the higher strength grades run up to minimum yield points of 51,000 pounds per square inch. (353 MPa) Further details of the steel making processes used in ship production can be found in reference 47. When a particular ship application involves extremely low temperatures, such as those for refrigerated cargo vessels or liquified gas carriers, special steels are required which have extra toughness and fracture resistance at low temperatures, as low as -165 °C. Many ships as we have already noted, such as cruise ships or say ice-breakers, require steel grades able to withstand service temperatures which are related to the lowest possible sea temperature likely to be encountered. When service temperature requirements are more related to the cooling of the cargo, such as for refrigerated cargo vessels or liquified gas carriers, even lower temperature ranges occur. Refrigerated cargo vessels usually need special steels which can withstand temperatures down to -29°C, whilst for liquified gas carriers, the cargo tanks and pressure vessels cooled by low temperature cargo may go down to -165°C. Between design temperatures of -55°C and -165°C, nickel steels are mainly used for the plates, sections and forgings which form these cargo tanks, secondary barriers or pressure vessels on board. There are appropriate nickel steel alloys, each with specific chemical compositions and heat treatments, available for any required design temperature, so that the correct alloy can be used for any intended application. Corrosion resistant steels are also available for cargo tanks which are used for the carriage of heavily corrosive liquid cargoes. In most cases the protective coating inside the tanks consists of a coating of stainless steel, which is *bonded* onto the structural steel which forms the tank boundaries. Types AISI 316, 316-L and those of extra low carbon content such as Type 316 ELC are also used in solid plate form, when relatively thin, and if the bonded varieties are not readily available. Type 316 is a standard 18-8, chromium-nickel stainless steel, which has been modified by the addition of 2 to 3 % molybdenum. This addition significantly improves its mechanical properties at elevated temperatures, and greatly increases its corrosion resistance. It is manufactured by the electric-furnace process, is non-magnetic when annealed, and it is not hardened by heat treatment. Type 316 possesses the highest creep and tensile strengths at high temperatures of any of the other stainless steels commonly used in shipbuilding, and is particularly resistant to the corrosive effects of salts such as sulphates and phosphates and other reducing acids.

Other marine applications can be found in the mobile offshore drilling industry, particularly where main structural members intersect, or where locked-in welding stresses are sometimes present. The more conventional steels used in marine structures may not be always sufficient to withstand "lamellar separation", which can occur when there are heavy transverse loads imposed at structural joints. Typical examples of lamellar tearing in a main plate Tee-joint connection are shown in figure 21. Here the horizontal plate has torn apart, at right angles to the vertical plate which was welded to it by two fillet welds. Under vertical load, the conventional horizontal steel plate may not be able to withstand the internal forces tending to pull it apart, in way of the welded joint. Special steels have therefore been developed which have improved resistance to lamellar tearing. These improvements are achieved in the melting stage of metal production and subsequent heat treatment processes.

Self Unloaders and other internationally used types of bulk carriers, which form another ship type, use special steels for resisting the abrasive effects of loading and unloading of cargo. The non-weldable type,

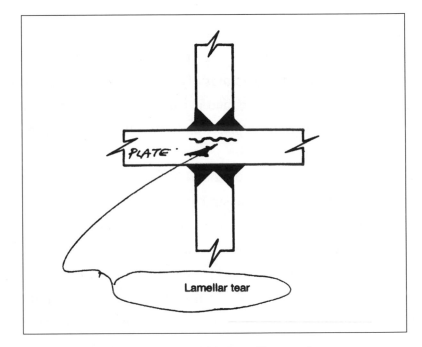

Figure 21   Sketch of a Tee-joint with lamellar tearing.

with high levels of carbon, manganese and chromium is not however generally used in marine structural work, most of that being covered by the type ASTM A-514 in the standard structural condition. A-514 may also be quenched and tempered for superior abrasion resistance and hardness.

Welding of steel, as commonly practised in many shipyards, is generally performed in ways similar to those already described for aluminum and other non-ferous alloys. At the assembly site, a manual welding process is still often used for making local connections, using a hand-held covered electrode, which shields the metal from the atmosphere during metal transfer and solidification.

The same equipment is also used for local cutting and burning of plates, bars and angles. Automatic or semi-automatic welding is performed by the TIG or MIG processes, both requiring an inert gas to shield the molten weld area and the arc from the atmosphere, which performs the same function as the covered electrode in the manual process. The inert gas employed in both processes is either carbon dioxide, the cheapest to use, argon, helium, or a combination of several such inert gases. In some applications of these welding methods, the filler wire is provided with a flux located in the central core, which acts in a rather similar manner as the covered electrode, to protect the weld from the effects of the atmosphere.

Another welding process for steel is the submerged arc method, whereby the welding zone is completely buried and shielded by a granular flux, which when molten maintains a high current density and concentrated source of heat. The base metal, as well as the consumable electrode, are both deeply melted with the intense heat so that high welding speeds and high deposition rates are possible. The welding speeds and deposition rates can also be further improved by using two or three wire electrodes, instead of the more conventional single wire type. Submerged arc welding is therefore the method frequently used in the automatic welding of steel for ship construction. Pre-fabricated construction units in modular form, completely piped-up, mechanically assembled and wired for electrical connection, and ready for erection at designated areas of the completed ship, are routinely automatically welded by this submerged arc process. Welding can be either from one or both sides of the work. If the quality of the work, its fairness, joint alignment, plate thickness and other properties are within acceptable limits, good welding can be performed from only one side, using a backing plate to contain the melted metal at the root of the joints. If there is plate waviness, more usual with thinner plates, good quality welding can usually only be obtained by welding from both sides of the work. This necessitates turning the sub-assemblies over to weld the second side, which can be time-consuming, awkward to perform, and lead to assembly distortion. Other welding methods such as the electroslag and electrogas processes, use adjustable copper shoes at each side of the welded joint. These retain the molten weld metal within the narow limits of the shoes, and thus permit even higher weld deposition rates. Because these processes have high deposition rates and result in large weld pools, they are usually confined to vertically welded joints where any excess melt metal is free to fall from the weld pool.

CHAPTER VII

AS SHIP FINANCIAL ANALYST

One very important factor which affects all types of ships, is that of ship financing. Every major exporting country provides long-term financing to foreign buyers of its goods and services, or guarantees bank loans to the buyers for financial transactions made in respect of such purchases. Financing is generally provided by a commercially-operated enterprise, owned by the government of the exporting country. In Canada, this function is performed by the E.D.C. (Export Development Corporation), whilst in the United States the corresponding body is known as the EXIM Bank. Similar functions are performed by the E.C.G.D. (Export Credit Guarantee Department) in the United Kingdom, A/S Exportfinans in Norway, E.K.N. (Export Kredit Namnden) in Sweden, and HERMES in Germany, to name but a few of these better known financial institutions. In most cases, the *funds are disbursed directly to the exporters* of the goods and services, on behalf of the buyer, who is also generally the borrower of the funds. Financing for capital goods, such as ships, is available at terms which in most cases are negotiable, but which can vary considerably from country to country. The financing provided by these government-owned banking institutions is generally limited to the same extent that the purchases are of domestic origin, any balance of the financing required being either supplied by the buyer or loaned by commercial banks in the exporting country. In considering marine projects or any other capital intensive order, consideration is usually given by the lenders to the impact of the project on the exporting country's potential for future exports, and the extent of employment provided by the project to the exporting country. **Strict attention is always given to the technical and economic viability of such projects, and the ability of the buyers to repay the loan, and here the marine consultant should be well placed to assist the banks concerned.** The terms of the loan and the repayment period have varied over the years, from country to country, sometimes being as long as 20 years, although shorter time limits are now more general and in line with certain agreed international principles of lending. In order to cover the risk of non-payment by foreign buyers for certain goods and services provided by exporters, the government-owned banking institutions such as E.D.C., E.C.G.D., EXIM bank and others, will offer protection in the form of insurance. These risks of non-payment by the foreign buyers include insolvency or default by the buyer, foreign government blockage of exchange of funds, changes in import/export regulations and similar hazards of doing business overseas. Generally speaking, the coverage extends to 90% of such losses incurred which are beyond the control of the parties to the transactions. These risks may be due to either political or commercial reasons. The balance of 10% of any such losses is usually borne by the exporters. Most exporters of such items as ships or associated capital goods, will use credit insurance programs of this nature on a specific basis, although Turnover Policies are also available. These latter policies provide exporters with multiple-country insurance, the premiums being payable on a monthly basis. Each country risk is evaluated separately, the maximum amount insured being generally at the discretion of the exporter's expectation of doing business in each particular country. Credit periods covered by this sort of insurance are usually between 180 days and up to a maximum of five years.

Some marine exports of capital goods and associated services often involve more than one supplier, and a working consortium is sometimes formed for specific projects. Surety insurance (100%), can be arranged to cover the *non-performance* by one or more members of the consortium, so that the other members of the consortium are not unfairly penalised. Penalties in such cases could often result in the call of a performance bond by the foreign buyer, in which case the insurer takes full responsibility for payment. Sometimes a foreign buyer will *wrongfully* call in a contractor's bond. Up to 90% insurance coverage can usually be arranged by the contractor to allow for this contingency. The banking institutions will usually provide 100% insurance cover to commercial banks against a call on a performance bond, issued to a foreign buyer on behalf of the contractor. They will also provide insurance cover to domestic surety companies who have provided partial coverage of the risk through performance bonds. Although not so frequently required as the foregoing, some overseas projects rely on input from suppliers or contractors from other countries, or from the buyer's country. Arrangements to provide some insurance coverage for this situation can often be made by the exporter. Surety insurance provided by the government-owned banking institutions, assists exporters who are required by the buyer to provide performance bonds and security for down-payments on a project. The surety insurance programs will protect commercial banks, surety companies and similar financial institutions, who normally supply the guarantees to the buyer. All of the foregoing risks referred to are usually covered by such programs. In the fisheries sector, with the rapid increase in joint ventures which occurred from 1970 to the 1980's, some exporters themselves became involved in investing overseas, by providing equity in the form of goods and services. For such joint ventures, the delivery of fishing vessels, personnel and ancillary services constitutes an overseas investment which may usually be protected against the following political risks:

- Expropriation of the capital goods
- Losses due to war, revolution or insurrection
- Inconvertibility, or being unable to repatriate funds to the exporter's country

The major criteria used to govern the eligibility of such project investments for surety insurance, is that **both the exporter's and the importer's country will benefit from the investment.** Up to 85% of the total risk is usually carried by the government-owned banking institutions, the insurance term covering up to 15 years. The investor supplying the goods and services to the importing country is usually expected to carry the remaining 15% of the risk against those risks itemized in the foregoing text.

Good examples of risk assessment arise in most developing countries that now control major fishing grounds up to 200 miles from their coastlines, but still often lack the investment capital, technological skills and equipment necessary for the effective harvesting of such resources. In these circumstances the joint-venture relationship referred to earlier is often the most effective solution, provided sufficient safeguards are introduced into the working agreement between the parties involved. Many fish resources available from developing countries have not always been able to be utilized for human consumption within the countries concerned. Mechanically de-boning or mincing of fish has been found to offer immense possibilities for the transformation of such fish, not traditionally caught or eaten. High protein, minced fish can be utilized as the basis for many finished and semi-finished processed foods which are acceptable to a wider range of consumers, and which can meet the increasing needs of an expanding world population. Parties seeking joint venture relationships in the fisheries sector expanded considerably in the 1980's, as the extension of national fishing limits up to 200 miles from the coastline, provided the acceleration to an already apparent international trend. The party based in the country owning the fishery resources is generally motivated by rather differing aims to those of the foreign party to the joint venture, and an early recognition and reconciliation of those aims is required to avoid future problems. The domestic party to the joint venture relationship will generally be familiar with the existing fishery laws and practices within his country, have some domestic and possibly export marketing experience, will be encouraged to expand present operations up to the new limits by appropriate governmental incentives, and be generally urged to supply increasing domestic nutritional needs. The foreign partner to the joint venture relationship could be a fishing company or consortium having long-range vessels, experienced crews and management of deep-sea operations, extensive marketing experience, further investment capital available for the new venture, and assurance of a continued sale of future fish production from the venture. The success of the joint venture relationship, however, will be generally in proportion to the extent to which both parties' aims are coincident or non-conflicting. Disposition of the fish catches, domestically or overseas, is probably the key factor to be resolved, not only between the parties, but between them and the appropriate fisheries authorities where the joint venture company will be based. This factor becomes less important when the landed prices of the fish on the domestic market do not differ greatly from the recognized international levels, in which case both parties will be more motivated towards increased domestic consumption, thereby coinciding with national needs and aspirations. In the past, many countries have tended to concentrate their economic effort in the agrarian sector of their economies, often at the expense of the fisheries sector, which could often provide significant increases in ready availability of protein. The problem has not been eased by the fact that traditional eating patterns in many developing countries have not included fish or even fish products as a major staple food source, except perhaps adjacent to their coast lines, where small scale, in-shore fisheries often exist. Distribution of fish and fish products throughout the interiors of many developing countries is still probably the main stumbling block to future domestic fish consumption. However, with the development of machines able to de-bone or mince fish and to derive in excess of 60% more fish flesh than from filleting machines, there exists a potential for not only increased protein production from accepted fish species, but also from those not presently accepted for human consumption. The many "look-alike" fish products available at most western supermarkets today, such as crab, lobster and similarly high-priced fish species are also proof that these methods of fish trans-formation have customer acceptance and are here to stay. The de-boning method also lends itself to continuous and mechanised food processing, food formulation, species blending, and food preservation, by using addi-tives in the processing procedures. The Japanese processing technology which produces "surimi" and "kamaboko" for their domestic market is just one more example of the means which can be applied by other countries having fish species in sufficient quantity to be able to produce minced fish and further processed edible products. An important aspect of this still relatively new fish food technology, is that such products and processes should generally be tailored to suit the tastes and prefer-ences of the consumers in particular countries, rather that to attempt to market products acceptable in one country, which may not have customer acceptance in another. The overseas investor will be influenced by many factors when selecting a country in which a joint fishing venture could be based. The availability of the fish resources and their suitability for intended sales, are probably the most important factors in deciding on the base country of operations. The overseas investor will also be concerned with the management of the fish resources by the host country, and the extent to which their future is safeguarded against over-fishing. Although it is obviously not possible to provide guarantees to fishing entrepreneurs that fish supplies will be maintained, it is possible to legislate for minimum quotas of fish catches to specific owners or vessels. The Inter-American Tropical Tuna Commission is considered one of the best examples of such a well managed fishery resource for yellow fin tuna, although still capable of further improvements in relation to vessel size. (Ref. 35) Fishing methods most often employed in large scale, commercial enterprises are stern trawling, such as practised by the large factory type vessels, and purse seining, as practised by the large tuna vessels mainly fishing in the Pacific Ocean. Stern trawling or fishing over the stern, can be practised using either bottom or mid-water trawl gear, and the fishing arrangements are such that change-over from one to the other type of gear can be easily made. (Ref. 36) Purse-seining is practised for the catching of tuna, herring and other shoaling types of fish, and the vessels employed for these operations can range up to 2,500 tons carrying capacity. The selection of the best fishing method for capture of fish species not previously caught in commercial quantities requires very careful evaluation. Research vessels can be of great value in making surveys and assessing the fishing potential of a particular species. These surveys will often contain detailed recommendations as to fishing gear, net sizes, towing speeds and depths of water to be fished in specific areas, all of which can be verified and upgraded as fishing operations by the joint venture company are expanded. As is well known, several attempted joint ventures have failed, because both the availability and abundance of the fish resources were over-estimated by the parties to these joint ventures. In some countries, more specific catch information is available from local fishermen who can be recruited to pin-point sea areas where such species have been caught, perhaps incidental to the catching of other species. Problem fishing areas can also be identified with the help of oceanographic, marine insurance organisations, government agencies, and similar bodies who can often provide valuable data on the nature of the sea bed, currents, tides, wind and sea states and the position of shipwrecks and other pertinent information. Some of the species which have proved to be the most suitable for the production of minced fish, are Japanese pollock, Pacific hake, and Atlantic croaker, all of which are caught in large quantities. The pollock catches are the most prolific, and used extensively in the production of surimi, with the balance being used in the fish meal trade.

Probably the most difficult commercial projects to assess for risk are those which involve international financing, and which include several partners, and have a complex infra-structure. Marine projects which fall into this category usually cover a wide range of expertise, including ship operations at sea, ship to shore cargo handling, shipbuilding methods, marketing of products and services, inland transportation, refrigeration, as well as the insurance requirements of the project, which need to be covered along the lines of those already discussed. For example, it is not unusual nowadays, for a project to have two or more ship-owning partners in different countries, to build the ships in a third country located thousands of miles from each of them, operate the ships on a world-wide basis, and have the whole project financed by an international group of banks, with the insurers being a combination of underwriters, insurers, and Government Agencies from several different countries. In the event of a default by one of the parties, it may not always be a simple matter of calling in a bond. I have found also that many bankers are diffident about marine projects, often because of their bad experiences in the past, when they simply did not assess the risks properly from the outset, and *failed to call in the required expertise* when the project was first mooted. There are also many cases on record where the bankers concerned have relied too much on having guarantees and insurances in place, when what was really required was *a complete evaluation of project viability*, which they wrongly took for granted from the borrower's application, without getting the benefit of independent, expert opinion. **Surely if they end up owning a business in which they have absolutely no expertise, as they often do by the default of the borrower, they would be better off to check things out from the beginning, before committing the bank's funds to the project in the first place.** This lesson is still being painfully learned even by some major banks, and not only in the fisheries sector, as they try to liquidate their reluctant ownership of failed ventures.

I remember one such project which I was asked to investigate in South America, on behalf of a well-known banking organisation, which had come to a complete stop, halfway through the project. This involved a capital expenditure in excess of 20 million U.S. dollars and required the building of fishing vessels, on-shore fish plant, a fishing port, and dock-side facilities for servicing the vessels and their equipment. I cannot go further into the details of the project, except to say that after an on-site evaluation lasting about one month, the remedies became clear to me, and as far as I know, everything was put back on track within six months of the evaluation. Such capital-intensive projects can also be part of international aid programs in developing countries, and these require very careful evaluation by the agencies concerned, since such projects may often be linked to socio-economic problems in the area where the aid is being contemplated. It is therefore often the case that several specialist companies will be invited to make proposals for carrying out the project in the recipient country, the successful bidder being responsible for its complete implementation, the training of local personnel and the setting up of the associated infrastructure for the project. All of this work requires a great deal of patience and sensitivity by those employed on the project, since in many cases the project itself may cut across old, traditional ways of working, or introduce new problems not originally contemplated when the project was first initiated.

The reader will have noted that to be an effective marine consultant involves a lot more than just a technical knowledge of ships, since we should be aware of their economics and profitability, as well as their operation in the particular trade in which their owners hope to make a living. Some naval architects have made a fulltime career out of conducting technical and economic studies for ships.. It was for those reasons that I have always tried to emphasise the importance of the detailed study of the *techno-economics* of any particular ship type with which we have been involved, since the technical and economic factors are mutually dependent on each other.

CHAPTER VIII

AS EXPERT WITNESS

Other interesting jobs seemed to arrive from out of the blue, one of them being by a strange route via Holland, starting from the U.K., and eventually set my course onto a third career. As I have described in greater detail in my companion book, "The Expert Witness", (Ref.33), I was approached by the lawyers for the Plaintiffs in a case involving the total loss of the upbound ship M.V. TRANSATLANTIC which, in 1965, was struck by the downbound ship M.V. HERMES in a 550 feet channel situated in Lake St. Peter in the St. Lawrence River. The claim was well in excess of five million dollars, and since it involved loss of life, the sinking of a large-sized vessel, and an extensive salvage operation to raise the vessel, was considered a major disaster of that period. The senior counsel who engaged me, were Stuart Hyndman, Q.C., Jean Brisset, Q.C., and Frank Gerity, Q.C.. They represented the three cargo claimants and were well advanced into the case when they decided that they needed the services of a hydrodynamicist. After some enquiries, which led them to the Ship Research Establishment in Wageningen, Holland, they were delighted to find that the expert originally recommended to them in England was, in fact, living within their own jurisdiction and in Montreal! This case proved to be the forerunner of a whole series of forensic investigations for which I was engaged, during the course of the next 30 years or more, *and still am!* The TRANSATLANTIC v HERMES collision case is a classic, since it involves several interesting points of law and also pointed the way forward to the proper use of experts in the maritime law courts law. (Ref.34) My investigation involved the calculation of the forces which acted on one of the ships, the HERMES, when in close proximity to the bank, which in this case was one side of the channel in Lake St. Peter, in the St. Lawrence River. These forces, known as bank suction, were shown to have resulted in the violent sheer across the channel into the path of the oncoming M.V. ATLANTIC. The verdict of the trial judge the Honorable Justice Noel, was favourable to our clients, the cargo claimants, who later called upon my expert services on many other occasions, as I have described elsewhere. (Ref.33)

On another occasion, I received a 'phone call from Edgar Sexton, a well known lawyer in Toronto, who requested my services regarding the sinking of the vessel "MIRIANA" in April 1971, in Montego Bay. This proved to be the start of a most intriguing forensic investigation into its rather mysterious loss, with a rather bizarre ending. The owner of the vessel had originally purchased her in a Government auction, at a good price. She was originally named H.M.C.S. "NORANDA", one of the "Bangor" class of offshore vessels, which were built in a series for the Royal Canadian Navy. They all had 9 cylinder, 2 cycle Diesel engines, driving a 3 bladed propeller, and in consequence had all suffered from excessive engine-induced, hull vibration, which in turn led to extensive repair bills over their lifetimes. MIRIANA was about the last one still in service, when I was retained to investigate her loss in 1971. She had a long history of cracked and loose rivets in the outer bottom plating, in way of the bilges, which required plate replacement on a more or less annual basis from 1946 to 1959, and beyond. At the time of the sinking, MIRIANA was 29 years old, since she was built in 1942, during World War 2. She was therefore 4 to 9 years past her normal life expectancy, and susceptible to hull deterioration, quite apart from the unusually high levels of hull vibration, which seemed to be most severe in the region of the lower bilges near to the Engine Room. I was given to understand later that the vessel's insurance policy had permitted pumping of the bilges whilst at Montego Bay, but that otherwise she was not insured for further voyages, unless certain modifications were made to the vessel. According to my recollection of the events at that time, the vessel left the shelter of Montego Bay, near the yacht club, and proceeded to anchor offshore for the permitted purpose of pumping out the bilges. A three-man crew then left the anchored, unattended vessel overnight, intending to return the next day to bring her back to port. During the night, a bad storm blew up, during which the MIRIANA disappeared from her station. The owner made a claim against his insurers for the constructive total loss of the vessel. The insurers first made the charge that the vessel was not properly insured, and that the premium had not been paid. This apparently was not so, and the insurers then had to face up to the fact that the vessel had sunk, whilst at anchor, and had a valid insurance cover. My report for the owner involved the analysis of factual evidence provided from service records of the vessel, reports of shipyard repair personnel over a long period, weather reports in the sea area of Montego Bay, survey reports of several companies who have assessed the vessel prior to sinking, and a report by the classification society concerned. I was also provided with design and working drawings of the vessel, as she was built. The first report by Lloyd's Register of Shipping, Montreal, in May 1942, included a list of defects discovered during their first annual survey of the vessel, and a list of proposed remedies to such defects, which had arisen within one year of its construction. This report noted that certain areas of the plating showed evidence of active corrosion, buckling of plates, leaky rivets and similar defects which had occurred in the lower portions of the shell plating, in way of bilges. These types of defects were further confirmed by shipyard surveys of the vessel, over the years. In June 1969, the vessel grounded whilst on a voyage from Halifax, Nova Scotia, to Toronto, Ontario. As far as was known at that time, the damages sustained by the vessel to the bottom plating were only temporarily repaired, and were never completed prior to the loss of the vessel. Again, in 1970, the vessel was involved in a collision with the tug "EL RENO GRANDE" and suffered damages to her topside superstructure, which were not repaired prior to the loss. I therefore considered the possibility that at the time of the loss, the bottom plating was in a deteriorated condition, and that it might well have failed under the action of excessive forces in the anchor cable, whilst riding at anchor in storm conditions. My calculations of the forces in the anchor cables, based on my earlier work for the Commissioners of the Port of Calcutta, India, showed that in the wind, sea and current conditions prevailing during the night of the loss, the combined forces on the bottom plating were sufficient to cause their collapse. This argument was reinforced by the fact that the hull plating was corroded below accepted thicknesses, and that deformation of the bottom plates, known to exist because of previous groundings, can cause weakness of plates when under compresssion. **I still wonder if all this factual data on the MIRIANA, and her sister ships, was ever factored into the risk assessment of the original marine insurance policy. If not, it certainly should have been!** A detailed report on this investigation, based on the foregoing hypothesis, was sent to the owner on payment of our final invoice. After that we heard nothing! Only six months after sending our final report, did we finally hear the full story from Frank Gerrity, the famous Toronto lawyer who had represented the insurance interests in the claim. The claim had apparently been settled for a sizeable sum, despite some late misgivings by the insurers that it was contrived, and not altogether a bonâ fide situation. However, the matter did not stop there, since the owner had promised his lady friend that they would marry, when his claim was settled, which of course it was. When challenged on this question, he apparently laughed at the idea, where-upon the lady was said to have pulled out a gun from her purse and shot him dead! Since we never did hear from our Client, who was always such a good correspondent, and also since we never heard anything to the contrary, I can only assume that this unhappy story was the reason that we never heard from him again. The first lesson to be learned from this story is of course that one should never treat matters of the heart in a facetious manner, otherwise you may not live to regret it. The second lesson, already referred to in my book "The Expert Witness" is that marine insurers should be prepared and willing to engage a highly qualified technical expert to assess *the risk attached to any major policy, before a claim has arisen*, otherwise they will find out too late that their exposure has been too great in relation to the premiums paid.

The MIRIANA case is a good example of how the poor service reports for the vessel although available, were not used properly, if at all, to assess the risks involved. This lesson is still not as widely understood or appreciated in the insurance industry as it should be, nor is the fact sufficiently known that a good marine expert working directly with the claims department, during the course of settling a claim, can often mitigate the loss to a very significant extent. It is also clear that there are many widely differing views in the marine industry on the best way to settle marine disputes. There is clearly a real need to address these matters, and the role that naval architects should play in them, so that all potential users of their services may be better informed (Refs. 33, 42). These users can be shipowners, shipbuilders, marine insurance interests or their legal representatives, and other claimants such as shippers and cargo interests.

The resolution of marine disputes does of course vary from country to country, and for example, in England, the court system has evolved in a rather special way. In London, there is of course the two-tier system of barrister and solicitor, in which the solicitors prepare the briefs for the client, which are then presented to the courts, by the barrister. This system is now under challenge by some, and Lord Woolf's report on this legal system is highly relevant to what we are trying to express our views upon here (Ref.43). The American and Canadian systems of law, as is well-known, allow a lawyer to act in a dual capacity, both as solicitor and barrister, which has the advantage of possibly reduced costs but the disadvantage of possible influence on witness evidence or opinion. The decision as to the location of jurisdiction where legal disputes can best be settled, is often a key issue to be decided in the early stages of a marine dispute, and one which requires a wide experience of the various courts and their attitudes to previous cases. Chapter 15 of my book, "The Expert Witness", gives some views on the selection of experts for marine cases and how they can best serve the legal process, and advise the court of the physical fundamental laws which must be respected when providing their opinions. I also recommend readers to A.J. Rogan's paper entitled "Conditions of Contract- The Rules of the Game", contained in Reference 45, since it covers very well the relationships which exist between a shipowner and a shipbuilder, as well as between a shipowner and a ship repairer. It also needs to be better appreciated, that when a ship is to be built, there are usually naval architects on both negotiating teams, so that in that sense there is some common ground of understanding between them, on the technical matters involved. Legal differences can however arise in the formulation of ship contracts, when naval architects are not brought into the negotiating process in the early definition stages. When a new ship is completed and accepted by the shipowner, it will hopefully soon pass into service. During its operating life it can of course, from time to time, be involved in a wide variety of incidents which can vary from a constructive total loss, to a simple case of cargo damage. Between these two extremes, disputes can and do arise, even in the best of operating services. Fortunately, after some hard work and practical, in-court, appearances by a few of us naval architects working in the legal processes, there became an increased awareness, at least in Canada and the U.S., of our design and build functions, which also extend logically into the specialised branches of ship operation and control, which I have described earlier. Firstly we have the views of those who work in the Admiralty and commercial court systems, which provide the basis for formal judgements. These can of course be appealed at two higher levels, which can and does often result in protracted delays in dispute resolution. Secondly, one can take recourse to the arbitration process, which makes awards widely enforceable under the New York Convention, and which are not generally subject to appeal unless the parties have in effect been denied natural justice. In England, the 1996 Arbitration Act has confirmed that leave to appeal should only be given in rare and exceptional cases, and the parties are now free to exclude the possibility of appeal by agreement at any time. Thirdly, and in my view of increasing importance and benefit to shipowners, shipbuilders and underwriters is the mediation process. What has become known in Canada and the United States as "Alternative Dispute Resolution" (A.D.R.), is the way for shipowners and insurers to avoid heavy legal costs, possible civil penalties and time consuming legal processes. As is well known, the mediation process is not binding on the parties, except in the sense that any agreement reached will have contractual force. However it does require a non-disclosure agreement, that information disclosed by either party during the mediation process, cannot be used in any subsequent legal action of that dispute, should the mediation be unsuccessful. To my mind, the mediation process has the further important advantage that sometimes a single mediator with the necessary knowledge and experience can be appointed by both parties, to assist *them* to resolve the problem under dispute. Mediation can therefore often result in a speedy agreement between the parties, once the strengths and weaknesses of their positions have been explored before the mediator. The process is in fact very much akin to pre-trial negotiations, except that it takes place generally in the presence of only one person who must remain neutral, plus a mediator advisor, rather than a group of legal and technical experts from both sides. Mediation is therefore practised directly with the parties to a dispute, with or without lawyers being present, with a minimum of written statements being made, and without going through the totality of available evidence and the often long-winded, discovery process. On that topic, it has been my experience that the discovery process does not always reveal the basic facts to a case. Unless there is a technical expert present, questions prepared in advance can often be evaded or circumvented, and I have many times in the past been given the transcripts of the discovery process, when it became apparent that the lawyer concerned did not have the detailed knowledge required to pin-point the real facts. A skilled mediator can however, without detriment to either party, focus each of them on the key issues of a dispute, of which they may not have been otherwise aware. Again, in pre-trial discussions or negotiations between the parties, I recall many instances when it became very obvious to the lawyers for each party, that the expert for the opposing party had not fully explored the facts available but used what I refer to in my first book, as the "machine gun approach". (see

Ref.33 - pp.154). Current thinking by the judiciary in Canada, seems to be that many cases should not be allowed to over-burden the legal system, and that every attempt should be made to settle disputes before going to trial. This is of course where the mediation process could help, before invoking the more formal legal processes. It is worth pointing out here that in the mediation process, the parties are free to resolve their differences, *without an imposed solution* by the court and arbitration systems. Again, mediators do not have to be lawyers, and technical experts have a good track record as mediators, when their expertise is involved in the dispute resolution process. To preserve impartiality, pretrial discussions heard before a Canadian judge are held to preclude that particular judge from taking on the case, if it goes to trial. Some would argue that judgements should be based on *all* the available evidence, as well as taking into account the credibility of witnesses, and one wonders if there is not some room for improvement in this respect, more along the lines of the American system. Should the parties to a dispute, for example, be permitted to change their pleas before the trial judge, after having had the benefit of pre-trial discussions before a different judge?

Again, as held by Justice Noel over thirty years ago, in the famous TRANSATLANTIC v HERMES case we have already considered, it is not correct for the courts to exclude the appearance of expert witnesses by either party, just because an assessor is appointed by the court. This question has now been settled by the Supreme Court of Canada, and one is thankful that it has now been resolved in the interests of justice and common sense, and that both parties are now free to present their best evidence, and also present alternative expert opinions on the evidence of a particular case. Hopefully that judgement by the Supreme Court of Canada will soon be extended to jurisdictions in other countries

(Ref.44). It bears repeating also that naval architects are trained in all aspects of the ship design and shipbuilding processes. No other marine discipline has the need, or the detailed knowledge, required to understand all of its operational and economic functions as a working vehicle.

Perhaps it would help also to give some examples of the differences which can arise between a legal opinion and a technical opinion, since they are based on entirely different philosophies! No doubt that is why many cases go to appeal, or can leave the parties to a marine dispute in a state of general annoyance with the results of the court system. It is a fact that legal judgements, or even arbitral awards, depend for the most part on facts introduced into evidence. When these facts change, so does the judgement. Even the "weight" of the evidence can change from one court to another, depending on the perception of the trial judge. The history of the legal appeal process is full of cases which get overturned, either because of perceived mis-interpretation of the original facts, found by the appellate court, or of new facts being introduced on appeal, which were not known or put forward in the original trial. It would seem to be self-evident therefore that there is a fundamental difference in approach, when the facts are interpreted by an expert, who bases his opinion on the *proven* laws of physics which govern such events, and which arise, for example, in the case of a ship casualty. Provided the expert opinion is *truly* based on these proven physical laws, such as those of Archimedes, Newton, Raleigh, Weber, Froude, Reynolds, Boussinesq, and others, (even Boyle!), then the opinion should stand. Fortunately, this principle has already been accepted in judgements of some cases in which I have been involved, and I hope that it will be extended to other jurisdictions, before too long. A good example of these possible differences of interpretation of the facts, between a legal opinion and an expert opinion, might be a collision case. Let us suppose, for example, that observers on ship "A", moving at a stated speed and direction, give evidence to the effect that ship "B" made a certain change of course, at a particular speed. Observers on ship "B" however, give an entirely different story to the court, as to their speed, course and change of direction at the time of the occurrence, some time prior to impact. In that simple situation, judgement as to cause of the impact would have to rely almost entirely upon the perceived credibility of witnesses. Now let us suppose that expert hydrodynamic opinion is available to the court. The hydrodynamicists are the best qualified and able to demonstrate the truth of the matter. In this case, we will assume that calculations, based on Newton's Laws of Motion, show that the observers on ship "A" are in error, and that it would be impossible for ship "B" to have turned through the angle stated by them, in the time available to do so. If the calculations submitted to the court are *truly* based on Newton's Laws of Motion, then the experts for each party should be in agreement. If not, then the correct judgement as to cause, will have to rely mainly on the determination as to which expert is at fault, by not applying the physical Newtonian Laws *correctly*. This then, again would become a matter of the law and a legal judgement. The appointment of an assessor to the court, would of course be helpful in this scenario, and assist the court to make the right decision as to cause. Unfortunately, for example, under English law, the experts for each party could not necessarily have been able to present their evidence *at all*, and the technical matters of navigation would have been left to any advice given to the trial judge, by the assessor. Unfortunately, unless the assessor was a hydrodynamicist, or able to make the required calculations of manoeuvring performance and so establish the most probable path of each vessel, during these critical stages, the judgement could well be flawed. There are of course many cases on record in the various Courts of Appeal, where the assessor in the Appellate Court entirely disagreed with the assessor appointed by the original trial judge. In the case of marine casualties, it is therefore very important for an expert to show the court when one witness account is to be preferred over another, if one satisfies the physical laws of the incident, and the other does not. Naval architects, as a group, also undertake many ship design functions, based on the owner's mission requirements, and these need to be well understood by the legal fraternity generally, if some of the problems which I have enumerated are to be avoided. I have listed some of the subjects, which have been presented in papers to the Royal Institution of Naval Architects, London, by some of its members, as well as those presented to the Institute of Marine Engineers, London and the Society of Naval Architects and Marine Engineers of New York, N.Y, U.S.A. during the past few years.

1. **Merchant Ship Losses 1934-1993**
2. **Steady State and Transient Responses of Bulk carriers and Tankers in Random Seas**
3. **A Numerical Study of Hydrodynamic Forces developed by a Marine Propeller**
4. **Ice Blocked Propeller Performance Prediction, using a Panel Method**
5. **Flooding Protection of Ro-Ro Ferries**
6. **On the Contention that Bulkers and Tankers are too weak in Storms**
7. **The 1995 SOLAS Diplomatic Conference (on Ro-Ro Ferry Safety)**
8. **Recent research and operational experience relating to marine machinery condition monitoring**
9. **Offshore certification and the new legislation**
10. **The contribution of ventilation system design and maintenance to air quality on passenger ships**

11. **Latest shipbuilding techniques**
12. **Marine casualties**
13. **Experience gained from 50 years of marine failure investigation**
14. **Life safety management systems enhancing pasenger safety**
15. **Formal Safety Assessment (F.S.A.)-putting risk into marine regulations**
16. **Experimental Study of Containment Boom Behaviour in Waves**
17 **Applying 3-D Product Modelling Technology to Shipbuilding**
18. **Performance Database for Offshore Tug Supply Vessels**
19. **Transverse Dynamic Stability of Planing Craft**
20. **The Successful Production of a Competitive Fixed-Price Ship Repair Job**
21. **Titanic Defended**
22. **The Titanic and Lusitania: A Final Forensic Analysis**
23. **Bulk Carrier Safety**
24. **Cracks and Structural Redundancy**
25. **Naval Ships and Simulation based design**
26. **Double Hull Tanker Research, Further Studies**
27. **The Open -Top Containership**
28. **The Securing of Vehicles on Ro-Ro ships**
29. **Trimaran Ships**
30. **New management standards for ship operators**
31. **Collation of DNV's casualty information**
32. **Crisis and emergency management**
33. **The North Sea Platform Supply Vessel**

I hope that these papers and their titles, will serve to demonstrate the wide range and depth of knowledge available to legal professionals from these institutions, when they act on behalf of Clients in marine disputes. There is an interesting Canadian case,(Ref.46), which emphasises the essential role of the naval architect, and the legal consequences of not engaging one during the design and building processes, and *which extend much further to the operation of the ship in service*. This case involved the constructive total loss of a Russian Ro-Ro vessel which sank in a storm in the North Atlantic in 1982. The essential facts, described in detail in Ref.33, are that two deck-mounted, forward ventilators broke off in heavy weather, thus permitting water over the bow to enter below decks, and eventually to cause the foundering of the vessel. The court held that with respect to this loss, the shipowner's duty to excercise due diligence with respect to the design of the ship and its construction, was not discharged, simply by the employment of reputable and experienced shipbuilders. Furthermore, in the light of the applicable law and the evidence, the court ruled that the Defendant shipowner had not discharged the burden of proof, showing that due diligence was used to make the vessel seaworthy.

What service can the marine technical expert therefore best perform within this system of dispute resolution? The traditional role of the expert in dispute resolution, whether in Court or in arbitration, is to act as technical adviser to one of the parties, and if necessary to give evidence. Nowadays, this will almost certainly involve the production of a written expert report, and often a pre-trial meeting with the expert or experts employed by the opposing party to seek to limit and define the technical issues. If this task is performed efficiently with mutual goodwill, which may of course depend on the instructions from the Client, it can be extremely useful in saving time and expense at the trial or hearing. In Court proceedings, the Judge may occasionally sit with a technical "assessor" to assist and advise on the technical issues, should the Court deem that to be advantageous to the better understanding of those issues. This is possible, but rarely occurs in arbitration, although a tribunal of lawyers, or others lacking the necessary expertise, may appoint their own expert, who will not sit as a general assessor, but will rather produce an independent report upon which the parties will generally be permitted to cross-examine. In addition, of course, one of the principal potential benefits of arbitration is that the parties are free to choose an appropriate tribunal, and technical experts are increasingly being appointed as arbitrators. Sometimes, the parties will mutually agree on the composition of a neutral, three-man tribunal, including one or more technical experts. Users of maritime arbitration in London will also be aware that a high proportion of the full (practising) members of the LMAA are technical marine experts, rather than lawyers.

But it is perhaps as mediators or mediator advisers, that technical experts can offer the greatest service. Certainly, mediation as taught and practised by CEDR, the Centre for Dispute Resolution, in London, contemplates the possibility of joint mediation by, for example, a lawyer and a technically qualified expert. It is perhaps unfortunate that this method of dispute resolution is not currently used more often in the marine industry, but as mediation becomes more popular, as it is now doing, its potential flexibility and the benefits it offers to Clients will perhaps be better appreciated.

CHAPTER IX

THE WAY AHEAD

The way ahead is perhaps easier to perceive if we study the latest ship designs and those current most active research areas, which look promising for the future. According to these criteria, the main areas of interest in ship design and construction, at least for some several years to come, are therefore likely to fall under the following headings.

- **Even faster ferries, patrol craft and similar types**
- **Multi-hull ship designs - catamaran, trimaran and quadrimaran**
- **Ships constructed of composite materials**
- **More powerful water jets, as prime movers for ship propulsion**
- **Ships constructed in "kit" form, for assembly by others**
- **Development of new fuels for main engines and auxiliaries**
- **Further developments in Unattended Machinery Spaces (UMS)**
- **New materials for outfitting of ships**
- **Fast-freight coastal transportation**
- **New developments in port design, for transmodal operations**
- **New developments in the design of life-saving equipment**
- **New developments in computer control of shipping operations**
- **Independent project management of shipbuilding and shipping operations**
- **New types of vessels, working in ice and infested waters**
- **New marine developments in the control of Environmental hazards**
- **Ships with double skin construction**

Each of the foregoing will require the specialised services of naval architects, research scientists, and engineers of all associated marine disciplines. Recent developments in hull form and propulsion systems have made their impact on several ship categories, especially fast ferries, cruise ships and patrol craft. Large, fast, passenger and car ferries have been built to both catamaran and monohull design, with no clear-cut decision yet available as to the best choice. To some extent this will depend on the length of the run and the local climatic conditions. Although the twin-hulled catamarans have proved their superiority in beam seas, there is some evidence to suggest that the single monohull designs are more stable in head and quartering seas. Since the early 90's the large capacity fast ferry market has been dominated by the catamaran designs, usually built in aluminum and up to 100 metres in length. The competing monohulls have been built of high tensile steel with aluminum superstructure, and have reached sea speeds in excess of 40 knots on lengths of around 145 metres. For example, the MDV 3000 Jupiter class ferries, built by Fincantieri at their naval yard near Genoa, are reported to carry 1,800 passengers and 460 cars in the high summer season, a distance of about 129 nautical miles, in only three and a half hours. In the off seasons, when there are less tourists, the mix of cars and trailers can be changed from 460 cars down to 100 cars plus thirty 30 ton trailers, or other intermediate combinations of them. Much of the speed performance of these craft can be attributed to the use of a twin CODAG propulsion system, each with its own engine room. Each system consists of one General Electric LM 2500 gas turbine and two MTU 20V, 1163 TB73L diesel engines (Refs.55). The flexibility of the system is such that top speed performance, with all six engines on line, can be reduced down to 30 knots with all four diesels and one gas turbine running, and down to cruise at 23 knots when only the four diesels are engaged. The system is therefore flexible in the choice of combinations of prime movers, and also through power transference to a pair of steering and reversing water jets and another pair of Kamewa booster water jets. The power transference is through reduction gears to each of the gas turbines, and also to double-inlet reduction gears for the diesel engines, each driving their respective water jets. These LM 2500 gas turbines and the smaller LM 1600, made by General Electric, have proved themselves over many years of U.S. Navy applications to frigates and destroyers, and various fast ferries and yachts in the United States and others in Europe. Several novel design features have been incorporated in these fast ferry designs to improve passenger and crew comfort, including the use of vibration and noise damping materials in the hull construction, silencers incorporated in the gas turbine and diesel air intakes and exhausts, and anti-vibration mountings fitted on the main engines, fans and air ducting systems. Active-type fin stabilisers, which are generally more effective than passive type stabilisers at higher ship speeds, have been fitted to reduce the rolling and pitching characteristics of these vessels in a seaway. Similar new developments are foreseen in the design of quadruple hulls, such as recently demonstrated by the four-pod vessel designed for the U.S Navy's Office of Naval Research, (ONR), by Lockheed Martin and Pacific Marine, based in Hawaii. (Ref.48) The main benefit of quadruple and higher order hulls, is that they can be designed to significantly reduce their frictional and wave making resistance at high speed, compared with other deep displacement hull forms. New developments are also likely to come from hydrodynamic lifting effects, which can be incorporated in the pod design. The overall power requirements to attain higher speeds are therefore reduced to feasible limits, whilst the dynamic stability of these vessels can be assured from considerations of the optimum pod and supporting strut configuration, both of which are likely to show further improvements.

Significant reductions in noise and vibration levels in cruise ships, and similar ship types where these factors are of greater importance, have been achieved by careful attention to the design of external propellers, and impellers working in tunnels. For example, companies such as Kamewa in Sweden, and others specialised in ship propulsion, have developed air injection systems whereby air is injected into the fluid volume around the impeller tips. Cavitation of these devices, which is a complete breakdown of the fluid flow, occurs whenever the local fluid pressure is less than the vapour pressure. This often results in severe loss of propulsive thrust, with attendant high levels of noise and vibration. Pressure-injected air systems however, form a "cushion" of air and water, which lowers the generated noise frequencies of the impellers at source. Further reductions in generated noise levels from impellers working in tunnels, and propellers working outside the hull, have been achieved by adopting highly-skewed blade sections. Skew is a geometric concept, whereby each radial blade section is arranged to progressively trail those of its adjacent inner section, as they are rotating. The sections therefore meet any high flow regions in a gradual manner, without the impactive shock which would otherwise occur if all sections entered these regions at the same time. For example, in the case of the American "ABC" ship propeller design (Ref.41), the angular intervals between the different blade section radii are as follows;

RADIUS	SKEW INTERVAL°
0.2 radius	1.5 degrees
0.3 radius	2.1 degrees
0.4 radius	2.4 degrees
0.5 radius	2.8 degrees
0.6 radius	2.7 degrees
0.7 radius	2.7 degrees
0.8 radius	4.4 degrees
0.9 radius	

This progressive "skew" of the blade sections therefore has the effect of reducing the local pressures between the blades and the hull surface, or in the case of an impeller in a tunnel, between it and the inner surface of the tunnel. Despite the foregoing improvements, incipient noise and vibration from impellers and propellers, may still sometimes be transmitted upwards through the hull structure. Noise and vibration levels on many ships have also been reduced by increasing the rigidity and mass of the hull structure close to the rotating propellers or impellers. (Ref.26) Such reinforcement of the tunnel structure, or the steel sections close to a propeller, therefore provides effective means of reducing the vibrations induced in them, which in turn leads to reduced noise levels inside the ship. The noise and vibration levels acceptable for passenger comfort have been studied extensively by various Classification Societies, notably Lloyd's Register of Shipping and Det Norske Veritas. The latter, for example, have developed a system of comfort rating numbers (CRN), which provides a guide for the noise levels in different parts of a ship, which are acceptable to passengers. These include the public spaces and open deck areas, as well as the passenger cabins themselves. The location of the public spaces within a cruise ship, such as dining rooms, public recreational lounges, sports decks, aerobic exercise rooms and telephone booths, to achieve optimum acoustical privacy, is now of increasing importance. It has been found that some of these noisier public spaces should be located as far as possible in the after portions of a cruise ship, where ambient noise levels are generally higher than those forward, and they are therefore less likely to cause annoyance. Acoustical levels for passenger comfort can be achieved in many ways, the most obvious being to improve the insulation materials between cabins, and between cabins and any adjacent public spaces, if their proximity cannot be avoided. Damping of impact noise from games and exercise rooms, open games decks, and galleys is another factor to be considered early in the design stages of a cruise ship, as well as standard considerations of the damping of main engines and equipment. Resilient mountings for Diesel engines, gas turbines and other rotating machinery have therefore been used to reduce the noise and vibration levels at source. Many primary power sources, if too rigidly attached to the hull structure, can sometimes result in excessive noise and vibration transmission through the hull, through air-borne waves from the source, or by water borne emissions which extend from the power source into the fluid areas surrounding the hull. These latter noise emissions are obviously very important for other ship classes, such as fishing vessels, naval craft, customs surveillance vessels and ships engaged in geographic survey work, for which there is a continual demand. All of the foregoing ships are the subject of expanding research and development.

Fast passenger and car ferries are becoming of increasing economic importance to facilitate between-island traffic, and for traffic routes between mainland ports and offshore islands. Until recent years, these routes have mainly been served by much slower, conventional type monohulls, with the main emphasis on passengers and freight carriage. With increased passenger and freight traffic to these areas arriving by air, mainly based on vacational requirements, a need for complementary sea traffic from major ports has been created. There is also an increasing trend towards faster inter-coastal passenger, vehicular and cargo traffic, on account of increasing world population dynamics. The correct balance between the passenger, wheeled transport and cargo requirements needs careful study. This balance is often only finally determined by opening up a new route, but allowing sufficient flexibility in the original ship design to be able to make simple changes dictated by the service experience. On some routes, however, there may be known, large seasonal differences in the ratios of passengers to wheeled traffic or cargo, so that the design layout can be arranged accordingly. The points of entry and exit for wheeled traffic is one of the most important features of these vessels, and variants range from bow to stern, roll on-roll off, to angled, side-loading and un-loading ramps on the main deck. New developments in vehicular safety and protection from fire on board, securement and tie-down systems during high speed voyages, and anti-pollution control systems can be envisaged.

Passenger safety in the event of fire or collision is anticipated to be of increasing concern, and new developments are already coming on the market for evacuation of passengers and crew in those situations. Systems such as Viking, and others derived from experience with aircraft crashes, provide a fast evacuation of both passengers and crew. (Ref. 49) These systems are likely to be required in increasing numbers, as passenger traffic by sea continues to expand.

The carriage of freight by fast seaborne craft is a new modal shift which is also inter-related with the carriage of goods by road transport. On some routes, where they require to be integrated, the sea leg of the route may show significant overall economic advantages when its flow rate can be increased. On other routes, fast freight by sea may offer significant improvements over existing road transport, and can relieve road congestion and pollution problems. High cost freight, consisting mainly of parcel and postal packages, is most likely to benefit from these anticipated improvements in transit times. Areas where fast freight and cargo services are anticipated to offer economic advantages now and in the future are between the West Coast of Norway and Continental Europe, the whole of the South China Sea region, the Gulf of Mexico and the Caribbean Sea, several coastal stretches of South America, the Mediteranean Sea, the Sea of Japan and neighbouring coastal stretches to the south. Fast freight marine transportation will require special treatment of the cargo, for both stowage and handling, since it will be subjected to much greater forces in transit than are normally experienced at present day ship speeds. New developments in the stowage and handling of fast freight can therefore be anticipated, such as fast feeder container ships from Canadian East Coast ports to those on the Great Lakes. With the increasing economic importance of countries in South East Asia and South America, despite some recent financial set backs, it is most likely that shipbuilding requirements in those areas will continue to increase in the long term. This is mainly due to their relatively low labour rates compared with Western economies, so that shipbuilding, which is now more than ever a modular assembly process, will naturally tend to shift to areas in the South and the East, including of course China which is rapidly developing its shipbuilding capacity.

However, as discovered by several more enterprising marine design companies, there is still a niche market for the supply of construction packages which can be shipped overseas from Western and other more developed countries. These packaged construction "kits" are generally based on proven designs of smaller vessels up to 50 metres in length, and can be transported in whole or in part by container, ready for assembly in the countries where they will eventually operate. Construction kits are usually based on computer-generated designs, each plate being cut by computer controlled equipment at the suppliers plant, and ready for welding and assembly at the final destination. Suppliers of construction kits generally provide full logistic support and on-site supervision for the assembly process, so that a technology transfer is in effect part of the "kit" concept. These kits have been supplied for construction of vessels in both steel and aluminum, in the former case being plasma cut, shot blasted and primed, ready for welding at the overseas assembly yard. This concept is likely to be of continuing importance in several countries having vessel requirements, but which presently lack the shipbuilding expertise and computer-controlled equipment needed to cut the plates, angles, and pipes which form the assembly modules.

Several new developments can also be foreseen in the important economic regions where unexploited oil and minerals exist, such as Alaska, Canada's Northern Territories, Norway, Finland, Siberia and North China, where the coastlines are often ice-bound for most of the winter months. Many ports around these ice-bound coastlines are without any means of inland communication, so that inter-port passenger and freight travel becomes a possibility, as already exists on the shores of the St. Lawrence River and various coastal stretches around Newfoundland and other Northern regions. Environmental issues are naturally of increasing concern, and ships designed for these ice infested waters will need to fully satisfy the safety requirements imposed by the harsh climatic conditions. This has and will continue to create new forms of marine transportation, which are able to withstand the impactive ice forces, high winds, and low temperature conditions in which these vessels have to operate. Oil and chemical tankers for Arctic and similar type operations are now required to have double hulls. This can also be seen as an increasing design trend for bulk carriers and ice-strengthened barges, which will be required for the transportation of the more remote mineral deposits and metallic ores now becoming of increasing importance in the world economy. In parallel with the carriage of passengers and cargoes in ice-infested waters, there is likely to be an increasing need for ice breaking vessels, such as the latest multi-purpose ice-breakers from Finland. (Ref.49) There is an increasing preference towards Diesel-Electric plant for the main propulsion system, having the flexibility to cope with a wide variety of load conditions from open water to working in ice. Multi-purpose, ice breaking vessels can also be used in summer months in ice-free waters, for offshore supply and oil rig duties, or for the carriage of deck loads and container cargo between ports. Winter transportation of cargoes in Northern waters is therefore seen as an increasing trend, and this will require an increase in the number of vessels capable of working in severe ice conditions, such as the Russian nuclear ice-breaker which navigated to the North pole.

There is a continual search for new fuels for marine propulsion. In the small vessel field, there are alternatives to petrol and diesel fuel, which now seem to offer several advantages both in terms of economy and the environment. Liquified Petroleum Gas, (LPG), as an example, offers a high octane rating, with clean burning properties and lower exhaust emission than either petrol or diesel fuel. LPG consists mainly of propane, with smaller amounts of butene, butane and propene, which can vary according to the source of the fuel. Propane is widely used in North America and many other countries where natural gas supplies are not available, but which can be used for heating and cooking purposes, and supplied in portable steel containers. It is anticipated that its use will be expanded as a propulsive fuel for marine craft, due to various factors which are now better appreciated. Firstly, the specific weight of

The Way Ahead

LPG is only about 67% of that of petrol, so that there is a weight advantage in the reduced amount of fuel required on board, or alternatively the range of vessel operations can be extended by about 33%. There is also a significant cost advantage in favour of LPG compared to more conventional fuels, which can be especially attractive to fleet operators with high annual fuel consumption, such as those who operate frequent river cruise or barge operations. Another advantage of LPG fuel is that existing engines can be retro-fitted quite easily to run on this alternative fuel, or they can be so arranged that either petrol or LPG can be selected at will. Since LPG does not contain lead or varnish, engine life is found to be two to three times more than that of engines running on other fuels, mainly due to reduced engine wear on pistons, cylinder rings, valves and sparking plugs. LPG has a normal boiling point of -43 degrees Celsius, and must therefore be stored in pressurised tanks, to keep it in liquid form. However, storage tank pressures are not generally excessive, especially in low temperature conditions, so that LPG is most likely to become increasingly popular for both heating and power systems in more remote, cold regions. It is sometimes not fully understood, even by vessel operators and marine insurers, that LPG is only flammable within a narrow range of air content, so that ignition outside this range, with either too weak or too rich a mixture, is not possible. In my experience in Canada, the safety concerns for LPG fuel on board small craft, either for heating, refrigeration or propulsion equipment, have been overly exaggerated, especially when adequate safeguards can easily be incorporated in the vessel design.

For larger ships, unattended machinery spaces (UMS) are on the increase, and required by all classification society rules to have specific control and alarm systems, and other safeguards for each of the following items. (see Refs. 50-52)

- **Air compressors**
- **Controllable Pitch propellers**
- **Electric Generating Plant**
- **Inert gas generators**
- **Incinerators**
- **Main and auxiliary propulsion machinery**
- **Oil heaters and purifiers**
- **Steam Boilers and ancillary equipment**
- **Thermal fluid heaters**
- **Waste heat boilers**

Alarm systems are required to give both audible and visual indications of faults in each piece of machinery installed in the machinery space concerned, so that the engineering personnel should be aware that a fault has occurred, and can take the appropriate action. In cases when a machinery alarm has not been acknowledged in the space concerned, an automatic alarm is required to be sounded in the engineers' accommodation. Both audible and visual indications of machinery alarms are to be relayed to the bridge control station, so that the officer of the watch is made aware when a machinery fault has occurred, that it is being attended to, and also when it is rectified. In the case of faults in the main machinery, which require speed or power reductions, or the automatic shut down of that machinery, separate alarms for these faults are required. The general category of control engineering systems also includes several individual systems which are required to be examined in detail, and approved before installation. These include the bilge and ballast system, cargo pumping system, evaporating and distilling systems, elevator system, oily water separator system, steering gear system, lateral thrust unit and positioning systems, valve indicating systems, and others which depend on the particular ship to be automated. Fire detection and control is obviously of major importance, not only in the engine and machinery spaces, but throughout the ship. For machinery spaces, a fire detection and control unit is required to be fitted *outside* those spaces, so that a fire will not render them inoperable. This may be in the area of the navigating bridge, or in some other control position outside the engine room.

All of the foregoing control, detection, and alarm systems require hardware in the form of programmable electronic equipment. New sytems are coming on the market for marine applications, which use the latest developments in micro-chip and valve control technology. These three systems each have to be designed such that a single failure or malfunction of the electronic equipment will only affect one of these functions. There are corresponding quality control and plan approval procedures in place for the design, development, modification and installation of the software systems used in conjunction with the hardware systems. It is usually stipulated by the classification society concerned that technical and hardware support must be provided by the suppliers of each system, for a period of at least one year after installation, or until satisfactory completion of the first annual survey of the system.

Kockums Mekaniska Verkstadt A.B. were the early pioneers of automated shipboard equipment, more than fifty years ago. In the early seventies I was consulted by them regarding the application of automated shipboard systems to measure the stability of fishing vessels and similar craft in service conditions. As a result of that collaboration, in 1973 my company was appointed to be their Canadian Representative for a wide range of automated shipboard systems. This arrangement continued for over 25 years through other subsidiaries, during which period we sold and serviced many different types of their equipment in Canada and abroad. LOADMASTER, for example, calculates the stresses and bending moments on a ship's hull, for a wide range of service conditions. CHIEFPLAN is used by the ship's officers to monitor hull stresses draft and trim during the loading of a ship, in order to satisfy acceptable classification safety limits. LEVEL MASTER is a completely automated system for monitoring tank contents such as oil, water and other liquids or gases. Again, STEERMASTER is a modern autopilot system which completely controls the path of a ship both on a straight course and during a turn, making allowances for wind, seas, and currents during the operation. TYPHON is a well known and respected registered trade mark of Kockums Sonics, dating back to 1918, which covers audible signalling devices for ships and on shore plant required to work under a wide variety of hostile climatic conditions. Systems such as these are in increasing demand, as they not only make the operation of a ship much easier and better controlled, but they tend to eliminate many disputes which sometimes occur regarding the amounts of cargo actually loaded or unloaded at the quayside, and the quantities of fuel consumed or remaining on board as bunkers.

One of the worst problems of ships in service comes from the deteriorated condition of the piping systems on board. These can include the fuel, water, cargo pumping, hydraulic oil, and sewage systems and others, all of which may be affected by engine, propeller, and machinery induced vibrations which can be transmitted through the hull structure, as noted earlier. Other types of vibration, both vertical and horizontal, can occur in all piping systems due to the ship's motion in a seaway. When the ship is operating with unattended machinery spaces, (UMS), it is therefore of primary importance to ensure that piping which is prone to fracture due to vibration of machinery, is well secured and protected. This is especially important for the fuel systems, where a leaking or broken fuel pipe can be the source of engine room fires or engine and machinery breakdown. One solution, which helps to overcome the danger of fires initiated by leaking or fractured fuel pipes, is to adopt a dual pipe system, such as that developed by Giro Engineering in the U.K. (Ref. 53) This novel patented system, amongst others, shrouds the high pressure fuel pipe within a second pipe of equal strength. Any leakage of the inner fuel pipe, is therefore contained within the walls of the outer pipe, and drained to a collecting tank. With such systems it is important to ensure that the end fittings of both pipes are well secured to the engine fuel inlets, easily locked in place and leak proof, even when the inner fuel pipe is leaking. It is also essential that failure of the inner fuel pipe be indicated by an audible alarm, so that the ship's engineers can take the appropriate action, either to replace the inner pipe later, or to drain the collector tank. A level sensor in the collecting tank will actuate this alarm when a certain fuel level is reached. Any excess fuel pressure between the walls of the two pipes, due to the leakage, also triggers a visual indicator in the end fittings of the piping system, so that a defective fuel line can be detected by on-line inspection. A further advantage of the Duoline fuel system is that the outer pipe is an added protection against impact or abrasion damages, which can sometimes occur in service conditions. The system has been successfully applied to new engines for oil tankers, bulk carriers, and naval ships for military applications, as well as retrofits for a wide range of marine and industrial engines by leading engine manufacturers. It is also anticipated to be an expanding market, due to the increased need to avoid ship detention in ports caused by piping problems, and the requirement to reduce engine breakdowns of many of the older vessels, still now in service.

As noted earlier in Chapter 6, there is a continuing need for new materials in ship construction, many of which fall under the general heading of "composites". Many of these new composites are being developed to meet naval requirements, spurred on by the need to achieve reduced overall weight, radar avoidance, elimination of expensive corrosion and maintenance problems, thermal and sound proofing of ship ducting and piping systems, better thermal insulation standards, improved vibration damping characteristics and lower life cycle costs. Composite materials technology is therefore high on the list of priorities of several navies, notably in the U.S.A. and several EC countries. Just as space technology led the way to new developments in other branches of the aircraft industry, it is anticipated that requirements to meet naval warfare standards, will lead to the application of new composite materials for merchant ship design and construction. These new developments are most likely to influence the fabrication, erection and outfitting of specific areas of merchant ships, particularly for cruise ships, where fire, smoke and toxic fumes are hazards to be minimised, especially in areas extensively used by passengers. Some recent ship fires have further emphasised the importance of fire prevention at source, as well as the selection of fire resistant and fire retardant materials for public spaces.

Port developments are on the increase. These must be able to cope with the handling of higher volume, faster container traffic arriving from new, larger container ships in excess of 6,000 TEU, (twenty foot equivalent units). These large, long-haul ships serve the major world container terminals, but need to be supported by smaller, shallower draft container vessels, which can distribute their containers to other smaller ports not capable of entry by the larger vessels. These smaller, feeder container ships are often fitted with their own deck cranes, and can therefore load and unload deck cargo of all kinds, including containers, at ports which have limited cargo handling capacity. New developments for the computer control of deck cranes, able to reduce the spotting and slotting times for containers, are of increasing importance. MacGregor-Hagglunds for example have pioneered their Steadyline microprocessor-controlled power swivel, (Ref. 54), which is claimed to improve the cargo handling efficiency by up to 20%. When picking up a container or other deck cargo, the operator can set the control lever to the required final alignment relative to the ship. Steadyline is then able to adjust the cargo unit to this required alignment, and maintain it, regardless of crane movements, external disturbances such as windage, ship movements at the quayside, or impactive forces from knocks against the ship hatchways or adjacent cargo.

There is a significantly increased annual growth rate for long-haul container traffic, which is about double the present growth rate of the world shipping fleet. Much of this increased growth in long-haul container traffic comes from penetration by container operators into the carriage of breakbulk, reefer and liquid cargoes. On some routes, specialised reefer vessels have been designed to transport refrigerated food cargoes in containers, to meet the high refrigeration standards required from factory to warehouse. In some countries however, port development has lagged behind the planned introduction of the larger, long-haul container ships, so that increased competition between ports is anticipated, to handle this increased container traffic. Adequate cargo handling, in the form of large dockside gantry cranes, is therefore of major importance for the long-haul vessels, which are generally without their own craneage. Terminals for container ship operations will therefore tend to be selected on the basis of their existing and projected plans for new and larger cranes, their available depths of water to cope with the deeper draft vessels, and their ability to forward the containers to other destinations by rail, road and coastal sea transport.

All of these trends in cargo movement present new challenges to ship designers, especially as ship sizes continue to increase well beyond

Panamax limits, and beams often now exceed 32.2 metres. As ships therefore increase in overall dimensions, driven by attempts to reduce the unit costs of container transportation, there is considered to be an increase in the demand for higher strength steels and other means for reinforcement of the structure. These higher strength materials will likely be required on account of the higher local stresses due to the increased dimensions, the higher racking stresses due to increased beams and depths, the larger transverse deck openings being adopted for the carriage of containers, considerations of the higher forces on containers due to the increased stowage dimensions, and further considerations of hull panel stresses. With the advent of new rules for the handling of containers by stevedores, improved means of securing and releasing them are being developed and will continue to do so, as the pressure to reduce the turn-round times of container ships continues. Due to lessons learned from past extensive losses of containers, (Ref. 33), protection of the forward tiers of containers from head seas has considerably improved in recent years. However, it is still evident that some operators are not fully aware of the dangers of operating their ships beyond certain limiting heights for the forward tiers of containers, and the need to incorporate breakwaters into the design of the forward exposed deck, for container protection against head seas. High-stowing covers, such as adopted by the designers of the KALIMANIS, a 16,500 DWT. carrier, are a perfect example of the protection for the forward cargo, which should be provided against the effects of green seas. This vessel is thus able to carry wood pulp, containers and steel coils with complete protection against such seas breaking over the bow. (Figure 23)

The trend towards even larger long-haul container ships, leads also to higher ship speeds in service, and average speeds around 25 knots are likely to be commonplace. The smaller, feeder container ships are also

Figure 23   Photograph of M.V. KALIMANIS showing high stowing hatch covers.

Courtesy of Hanjin Heavy Industries /MacGREGOR news.

tending towards higher service speeds, in the region of 30 knots, which requires finer hull forms and multi-hull configurations in order to keep the main engine horse power within economic proportions. It is therefore anticipated that there will be an increased emphasis on the design of new hull forms and propulsion systems to meet these faster intermodal trends. These higher sustained sea speeds will demand even more attention to the care of the containers, their securement in service, both in the holds and on deck, the strength requirements of the forebody of the main hull to resist the increased impact forces from the sea, and the steering and course-keeping control of these faster ships in a seaway. Stability requirements will also influence the choice of hull configuration, since as depth, the least costly ship dimension, is increased to accommodate more containers, corresponding increases in beam are required to meet the same stability standards. There is therefore likely to be some scope for high speed, multi-hull configurations, having greater inherent stability compared with mono-hull designs, particularly for the smaller feeder container vessels.

Independent project management of shipbuilding and shipping operations is becoming of increasing importance. For example, some shipowners do not always have the "in house" expertise required to supervise the construction of their ships, either for new buildings or conversions. They therefore need the specialist services of a team of naval architects, marine engineers and others experienced in all the various aspects of ship design, contract writing for new buildings or conversions, drawing and class approvals, active supervision of construction, ship trial assessment, delivery approvals and obtaining all the required regulatory and flag approvals for such projects. Independent contract management for marine projects is therefore of great value to owners whose staff may only have a limited experience of dealing with shipyards for ship conversions or new buildings. Large differences in anticipated time of delivery and large order changes throughout a shipbuilding contract can sometimes occur, leading to costly delays, non-recoverable losses of revenue for the vessel and increased administrative expenses. These problems can be minimized by a combination of superior and experienced contract writing, coupled with methodical contract management procedures, actively managed by the independent project managers. Delivery over-runs and costly escalation of the contract price, often result in expensive litigation procedures. These time over-runs can sometimes result in the loss of a time charter, caused by a combination of incompetence by the contractor and lack of experience by the owner's representative. The risk of these contractual differences arising can be minimized by putting the following steps in place, right from the beginning of the project;

- **Integration of plans, technical specification and contract**
- **Writing the contract to avoid risks of mis-interpretation**
- **Writing the contract to allow for possible contract disputes**
- **Litigation, arbitration or mediation?**
- **Evaluation of contract bids and bidder competence**
- **Identification of inherent risks to owner and contractor**
- **Direct assistance during negotiations**
- **Defining the contract management procedures -step by step**
- **Monitoring the shipyard contract schedule**
- **Evaluation and negotiation of design changes on behalf of the owner, during the contract (Time and money)**
- **Post delivery settlement negotiations**
- **Provision of expert witnesses for contract disputes**

The luxury yacht field is just one example of the expanding market for project management. Vessel sizes between 45 and 90 metres are now quite commonplace, and new building costs of these vessels are now often in excess of \$U.S.30 million. The benefits to an owner of having the whole project managed independently, by an experienced project management team, can therefore be considerable, not only in keeping the building costs and time of delivery under close control, but in advising the owner on the safety, environmental, regulatory aspects and logistic support functions for the vessel in service.

There are also several well-known, established, independent ship management companies, who for a fee or share participation will run particular ships on behalf of owners who may have the capital, but not the expertise or connections required for a particular trade. Ship operations may also consist of a new combined venture, in which one partner supplies the ships and the other supplies the shore-based managers, ship's officers and crew with working experience of that particular trade. These arrangements are likely to increase as international competition intensifies, as has already occurred in the container trade, and as the smaller operators become less competitive.

CHAPTER X

EPILOGUE

I have tried to show the various roles in which naval architects can practise, partly through describing some of my personal experiences over the last 50 years or more, and partly by drawing on the wide background and extensive literature of the subject of naval architecture. (Ref. 42) As with all professions, there are generalists and specialists, and I had the unique experience of practising first as a specialist in hydrodynamics, and then more as a generalist in a wide variety of consulting roles, including that of expert witness. Some naval architects of course never change direction, and many of my old friends and colleagues continued working in ship research at the N.P.L. and retired without ever entering the "hurly burly" life outside of that hallowed sanctum, or should I have said the sanctum santorum? It has been well said that the only consistency in life is change, and I have no regrets that I chose to pursue a full range of changing experiences in naval architecture, except that I had to leave the country of my birth to do so! The reason was that in the late sixties and before, there was unfortunately a rather indifferent attitude towards applied research in industry in Britain *at that time*, and many young people left to go to more enterprising countries, where they could better fulfil their careers. Nowadays, there is a noteworthy improvement in public and corporate awareness of the importance of marine research, worldwide. I hope also that some of the ways in which young people today can actively participate in marine research and development will be better appreciated, after reading the chapter on "The Way Ahead". I hope also that those responsible for the teaching of the subject of naval architecture will continue to place more emphasis on *combined* education and "hands-on" training, as was practised under the old Admiralty Dockyard system in which I was trained. In retrospect, this was years ahead of its time, and although rather ruthless in the way apprentices were selected for advancement in the system, it certainly brought the best to the top, as study of the rolls of the past presidents, council and and officers of the Royal Institution of Naval Architects, London, England will easily show! The same lesson applies to those who came to the top via the more commercial shipyard route, almost all of whom at one time or the other have had sea experience, coupled with shipyard training in ship construction or repair. I also remember very vividly, after a spell in Japan during the early sixties, being asked what I considered to be their biggest national problem! As they were then, at that time, building more than 65% of the world's ships and world leaders in many other engineering disciplines, I was somewhat taken aback, although flattered that they thought I might even have a worthwhile answer. My reply, since repeated on many other occasions in other countries, was "*communication*", and it is amazing how even today, with all the sophisticated means available to communicate, how seemingly simple messages have a habit of being so easily misunderstood. As any world traveller will confirm, it is truly amazing to see the growth of the English language in so many remote countries, which have discovered this importance of communication and who are training their young people in English at an early age, in order that they will not miss the economic prospects for the next millenium. I have no doubt, as I have already stated in my previous text, that the future of shipbuilding will continue its expansion to the South, the East and the South-East, much of it requiring a high level of computer technology, which seems to predominate in English. There is therefore

Epilogue

a continual need for educators to be watchful of the language, and to strive for high international teaching standards.

Again, anyone who has ever practised as an expert witness will know the importance of preparing clear and unambiguous reports for the court, and of the absolute necessity to be able to articulate and communicate that information to the court. Lack of communication in any one language, or between languages, is often the reason for legal disputes arising between parties who do not *fully* comprehend the real issues of a case. The mediation process, as a prerequisite to formal litigation in the courts, is another good example of how communication between the parties can be considerably improved by a skilled mediator, perhaps aided by a *mediator advisor*, who can focus each party on the key issues to the dispute, which they would perhaps otherwise only discover later in the court, at considerable cost! There is unfortunately a mistaken view held by some in the marine Industry, that clarity of written expression and verbal expertise are unfair weapons, not to be used by competing experts in the courts or in arbitration proceedings. (Ref.53, pp36) What rubbish! Do proponents of this doctrine perhaps wish us all to sink to their own level of linguistic inability, or to offer inferior written or verbal evidence, so that the issues can be clouded even more? As the good old American expression goes, **if you can't take the heat, get out of the kitchen**. I also remember from my former days at Durham University that engineers were thought to be, especially by those in the Faculties of Art, notoriously poor at expressing themselves either in written or spoken form. I wonder if there has been any improvement over the years? I think not. Nowadays, certainly in North America, people generally seem to have found a whole range and diversity of meanings for words such as cool, -great, -terrific, -neat, -wow, -brilliant, etc., none of which seem to be used in their proper context and can only lead to a decay of

155

our beautiful English language, the richest in word count and shades of meaning of any language in the world, if used properly. Nowhere is this clarity of expression and meaning of such importance as in *scientific and technical writing*. Engineers of all disciplines should therefore strive to improve their knowledge and use of the English language, and fashion it to meet the particular needs of the subject, whether it be report writing, shipbuilding and repair specifications, technical analysis, contract definition, risk analysis, evaluations of ship performance, or simply the interchange of data and information between the owners, builders, engine and equipment sub-contractors, bankers, insurers, and others involved in design, shipbuilding and shipping operations. In my view, Universities and similar places of learning who teach naval architecture, should include technical and scientific writing as an *obligatory* part of their curricula.

There is a large, relatively new market in all branches of science and technology for safeguarding innovations, whether they be in the form of patents, trademarks or unpublished material such as drawings, draft manuscripts, or indeed anything which is unique and can be defined in written form under the heading of intellectual property. This expanding marine market requires legal, scientific and technical expertise in order to provide full protection to clients composing innovative material, and also to protect those who may perhaps unwittingly breach existing patents or trade marks and thus expose themselves to legal action. Some marine experts may therefore be called upon to provide direct scientific and technical assistance to law firms engaged in writing intellectual property rights and contracts, or be retained by them and their clients to assist in composing intellectual property claims, for or against others.

Environmental issues are of increasing concern to many groups who may be affected adversely by marine activities, not only by shipping opera-tions, but for fixed structures such as oil drilling rigs, oil refineries and

Epilogue

their marine terminals, passenger and car ferry terminals, container ports, and many other similar coastal, riverine or offshore facilities. The well known Exxon Valdez, Sea Empress, Piper Alpha, Marchioness and Achille Lauro cases alone provide some idea of the magnitude of marine claims which can arise when large ships and marine structures are involved. Naval Architecture and other associated marine disciplines are therefore all likely to be required whenever shipping operations affect environmental issues. These adverse interactions are most likely to occur when other marine activities are also affected, as for example when coastal fisheries are damaged due to oil spillage from tankers, when inland oil spillages from refineries pollute yachts at marinas, or when public utilities are degraded due to chemical effluents, all of which have occurred in recent years. A wide range of expertise is therefore likely to be involved, in order to establish cause, and the nature and cost of the damages involved.

The analysis of marine risk is probably one of the areas of expertise least understood by both banking and insurance interests, who have traditionally tended to rely too much on documents and guarantees submitted by the borrower, or in the case of insurers, by the sometimes dubious opinions of a lead underwriter. The role of the *truly independent* marine expert in risk assessment is seen therefore as an expanding and demanding field of expertise, for the relatively few naval architects, who are so qualified and prepared to act on behalf of those at risk.

N.P.L. EXPERIMENTS ON LIGHT VESSELS

It was considered that the following factors required investigation, and that as many as possible should be recorded in the experiments.

- **Cable tension**
- **State of sea**
- **Pitch, yaw, roll, heave and distance of the bow of the model from the anchor**
- **Strength and direction of current**
- **Wind force and direction**

The experiments were made to compare the riding behaviour and cable tensions of two Light Vessels of widely differing form characteristics and longitudinal weight distribution, but having nearly the same overall length and beam. Model 3667 was made to the lines of a new light vessel (L.V. "Flame") designed by Messrs. Rendel, Palmer, and Tritton, and compared at the same wind, sea, and current conditions with Model 3749. This latter model was made to the lines of an old pilot brig (L.V. "Fame") which had served as a light vessel for over forty years, and was known to possess good riding qualities compared with contemporary vessels. Both models were made in wood, complete with superstructure, to 1/15 full scale, shown typically in Figure 9. The conditions of wind, sea, and current at which the experiments were to be conducted were decided upon from consideration of full scale data obtained in the Bay of Bengal area, particular attention being paid to the fact that synchronous pitching and heaving of the vessels tend to promote conditions where cable tension is a maximum. Synchronism occurs, of course, when the wave period matches the pitch or heave periods. Wavelengths in the region of 115 to 145 feet are experienced on occasion in the area, with associated mean wave heights of 5.5 to 8.25 feet, the wave system being irregular in amplitude. Current speeds vary between 0 and 5.5 knots.(0 to 6.33 m.p.h.) Although wind speeds of 80 to 90 miles per hour and above have been recorded, it was only possible to simulate 40 miles per hour on the full scale with the existing equipment, and this velocity was adhered to throughout the experiments. Both models were tested with a length of cable corresponding to 90 fathoms, and a depth of anchor of 5 fathoms, and also at 120 fathoms length of cable and an anchor depth of 10 fathoms, as these are the cable lengths expected to be clear of silt at those depths. (1 fathom equals 6 feet) In addition, the effects of elasticity in the cable were investigated with the model of the L.V. "Flame", Model 3667, having a spring mechanism fitted at the bow. The mechanism corresponds on the new, full scale, Light Vessel to one with a pre-loading of 10 tons, such that no movement at the end of the cable occurred up to this magnitude, at the point of attachment on the ship. Extension of the mechanism occurs from zero to 4.0 feet, for cable tensions between 10 and 50 tons. In an attempt to dampen the pitching motion and vertical motion of the bow, the bilge keels of Model 3749 were extended in depth by 50%, and the effects of this modification were determined with a cable length of 90 fathoms and an anchor depth of 5 fathoms. The model under test is towed on its chain cable at a series of constant speeds, thus simulating the effect of current speed, through a series of irregular waves generated at the end of the tank, by a plunger-type wave maker. The waves produced correspond to a mean length of between 115 and 145 feet, and their height and frequency conform to a pre-set pattern, which approximates to that which was anticipated in the Bay of Bengal under extreme conditions. The rudder angle of the Light Vessel was maintained at 35 degrees to starboard, to simulate full scale conditions when the vessel is yawed to the direction of the current, wave front, and wind direction. When towed at constant speed, *corresponding to that of the current on the full scale Light Vessel*, the model under test is found to oscillate about a mean yawed position, due to the interaction between restoring forces in the cable and the exciting forces from the wind, current, and wave action. During these model experiments, the following parameters were measured and subsequently analysed.

- **Cable tension, by means of electrical strain gauge**
- **Pitch, yaw and roll of the model, by means of gyroscopes**
- **The film speed of the camera, by electrical recorder, (so that all positions of the vessel could be synchronised with all other data). - Once again the Photographic Unit was able to arrange for these types of records to be taken.**
- **Wave height, by electrical probe.**
- **Period of encounter of the model with the waves, (so that wavelength could be calculated)**
- **Speed of advance, corresponding to current speed on the full scale.**

Figure 9 shows a typical model under test, being towed on its cable to simulate the effect of the current. It was found that the maximum cable tensions occurred when the horizontal motion from the anchor, and the vertical motion of the bow, both reach maximum values *simultaneously*. This is to be expected from theoretical considerations of the motion of the bow, and the effect of this motion on the configuration of the cable. The results obtained with model 3667, (L.V. Flame), show that peak values of cable tension occur when the period of encounter of the model with the waves, lies in the region of the natural pitching period of the model. There is marked reduction in cable tension, in the range where the natural pitching period of the model exceeds the period of encounter with the waves, and where the 90 fathom cable is at an anchor depth of 5 fathoms. This was found to be due to the reduction in vertical bow motion, and reduced pitch and heave of the model, compared with the longer cable length. The degree of slackness of the cable when the cable tensions were maximal, was found to be only of the order of 0.3 per cent, for current speeds between 4.0 and 6.0 knots, showing that some extra elasticity in the cable might be beneficial in reducing the cable tension. At lower values of cable tension, it is important to know the frequency of their occurrence, since this has an important bearing on the fatigue life of the cable. It was found that at the level of 15.0 tons of cable tension, for example, there were as many as 20,000 repetitive cycles per day. The shorter cable length of 90 fathoms was again found to be superior to the longer 120 fathom cable length, set at 10 fathoms depth.

The effects of providing additional elasticity at the end of the cable, by a spring mechanism secured to the fore-deck of the vessel, were dramatic. The cable spring mechanism, designed at the N.P.L., reduced the maximum cable tensions by some 30 per cent, in the region of 4.0 to 6.0 knots current speed. Another important factor, is that the gear used on the full scale Light Vessel, L.V. Flame, was *not* pre-loaded, so that chafing of the cable in the hawse pipe occurs at all times. When a pre-loading of 10 tons is provided in the spring mechanism, the cable end does not move until this value is reached, so that wear and tear can be considerably reduced. In order to prevent shock loading of the mechanism, when it is fully extended to its limit of 4.0 feet, the recovery period is arranged to be less than 50% of the natural pitching period of the ship. This ensures that it is almost always back in the primed position, when cable tension starts to build up.

The results obtained with the older Light Vessel, L.V. "Fame", (Model 3749), generally confirm the results obtained with the new vessel, except that a longer cable length of 120 fathoms, at an anchor depth of 10 fathoms, gives slightly better results than the 90 fathoms shorter cable. The effect of extending the depth of the bilge keels by 50%,on the older vessel L.V. "Fame", is generally to decrease the maximum cable tension over the full range of current speeds up to 6.0 knots. In the lower part of the speed range, from 0 to 3.0 knots, these improvements amount to more than 40%. It was found that these reductions in cable tension arise mainly from the reductions in motion of the bow, due to the damping effects of the deeper bilge keels.

In summary, we can see that these experiments show the marked superiority of the new design, L.V."Flame", which never exceeded 45.0 tons, compared with the proof load of the Tayco cable at 66.5 tons. On the other hand, the L.V. "Fame", the best of the old existing vessels, reputed to have good riding qualities, exceeded the proof load of the old, open-link, iron cable and closely approached that of the newer Tayco steel cable.

THE N.P.L. YACHT DYNAMOMETER

The models are towed from a point at the top of a dummy mast, erected in the model at an assumed centre of effort position of the sails, and a constant torque is applied at this point, on the vertical axis of the shaft. When towed at various speeds through the water, the model assumed a stable, heeled, and yawed attitude.(See Fig.7) The dynamometer was built into a framework and designed to work in the measuring bay of No. 2 Tank Carriage. The carriage is equipped with automatic speed control, and when on a constant setting, maintains the speed of the model to within less than +/-1/4 per cent. The upper end of the "dummy mast" erected in the model is fitted with a universal joint, which connects with a vertical shaft, 1.125 inches in diameter. The dynamometer is built around this vertical shaft, to which all the model yacht forces, acting in a horizontal plane, are freely transmitted at the measuring position. The measuring head, corresponding to the centre of effort of the sails, consists of a double air-bearing, surrounding the vertical shaft, in way of the universal joint. This double air bearing is supported on an air cushion at its lower surface, and air is also fed in between the shaft and the cylindrical surface of the bearing. Forces at the universal joint are therefore transmitted through the floating air bearing, on to two hydraulic bellows placed at right angles to each other. This system therefore ensures that almost frictionless axial and rotational motion of the vertical shaft can take place, whilst the forces in a plane at right angles to it are being measured at the centre of effort. The bellows are sensitive to axial compression, and are connected, via copper tubing, to glass manometer tubes. Changes in level of the coloured fluid in the system, therefore enable a direct measure of the forces applied to the bellows to be made. With this system, it is possible to vary the sensivity of the apparatus by using varying ratios of the sectional area of the bellows, or of the manometer tubing. Alternatively, the stiffness of the metallic bellows can be varied. A contraction is incorporated in the system, between the bellows and the manometer tubing, so that surges in the level of the fluid are dampened during the tests. The complete measuring head, as described, is capable of being raised and lowered by electrical push-button control. By these means, the operator can ensure that all measurements are taken with the measuring head in line with the centre of effort position of the sails. The upper end of the vertical shaft is attached to a cross-piece, which runs in roller bearings on two auxiliary vertical rods, mounted on a rotable plate.(see Figure 8). In this way, the vertical motion of the yacht model is unconstrained, whilst any out of balance moments on the model, (corresponding to the rudder moment) are mea-sured on a spring system fitted to the cross-piece. The vertical height of the centre of effort of the sails, (the centre of the air bearing), is measured on a vertical scale attached to the rotatable plate. The vertical component of the wind force, at the centre of effort, is applied directly to the vertical shaft. This is achieved by unloading the previously balanced, vertical shaft system, by removing a pre-calculated weight from the scale pan shown in Figure 8. The apparatus is also calibrated before each series of experiments, by applying a range of known weights to the model, both longitudinally and laterally, by means of weights and pulleys. The cali-bration of the various models tested shows very consistent repeatability. The spring and dial gauge system, fitted to the cross-piece, is calibrated in a similar manner by applying known torques to the vertical shaft.

The N.P.L. Yacht Dynamometer

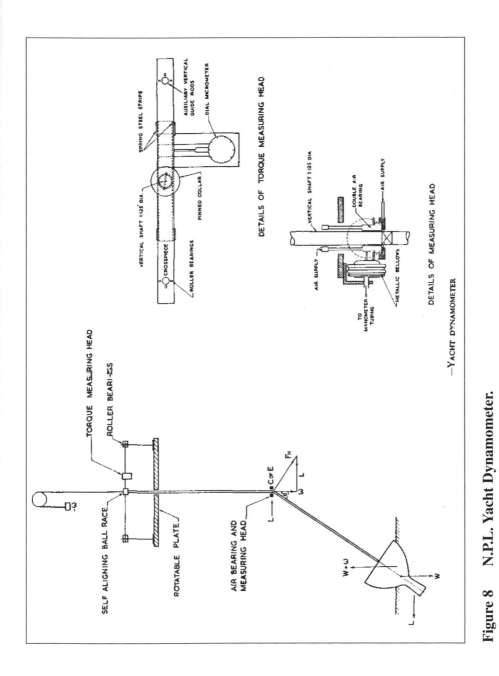

Figure 8 N.P.L. Yacht Dynamometer.

The Naval Architect

The yacht models are made of wood, and the scale of the model is chosen to arrive at a model length of about 5.0 feet. With this testing system, it is essential to manufacture the models with the correct scaled-down position of the centre of gravity of the full scale yacht. The "bread and butter" system of construction is used, each joint being glued and screwed. In order to give as much movable ballast in the model as possible, to achieve the correct balance, it is essential to keep the weight of the main body to an absolute minimum. The keel is made of lead to give a low centre of gravity, and shaped, with the aid of templates, to fair in with the main hull. The complete model is then suspended on lugs, attached to the hull on an axis through the required centre of gravity. By shifting the movable ballast weights within the hull, it is possible to arrive at an equilibrium position, when the centre of gravity of the combined hull and keel are coincident with the axis of suspension. Due to the long test periods for which these models are often required, several undercoats of paint are applied, and repeated rubbing down is performed to ensure a durable smooth finish. Turbulence stimulators, which consist of 1/8 inch diameter studs, projecting 1/16 inch clear of the hull surface, are fitted below the waterline in the fore body. These studs are spaced in a set pattern, 50 in number, to ensure fully turbulent flow. Tests were made of two models, with and without these turbulence stimulators. The results showed that beyond a certain model speed, the flow over the hull surface became fully turbulent, and that below this speed the flow was transitional in character, i.e. part laminar amd part turbulent. What was very revealing also, was that the relative performance of the two models, with and without turbulence stimulation, was completely reversed. This lays emphasis on the importance of ensuring full turbulence over the models, which is a stable condition, and which can then form the basis of full scale predictions of yacht performance.

CHAPTER XII

LIST OF REFERENCES

1. "The Ocean on a Plank"-Captain W.A. Doust. C.B.E. - ISBN 0--85422-0887, Printed by Western Printing Services, U.K. , also Seely, Service & Co. 1976.

2. "Mud Muscle, and Miracles"-Marine Salvage in the U.S.Navy, -Captain C.A. Bartholomew, USN-Department of the Navy, Washington, D.C.1990 ISBN0-945274-03-3

3. "Side launching of ships-with special reference to trawlers" D.J. Doust -Trans. Royal Institution of Naval Architects, London, U.K. 1955.

4. "Further experiments on sideways launching"- D.J. Doust and E. Macdonald- Trans. Royal Institution of Naval Architects, London, U.K. 1957.

5. "Side launching on the Great Lakes"- J. H. Fahey, Trans. S.N.A.M.E. Vol.50, 1942.

6. "Riding qualities of Light Vessels"-Lt. Comdr. E.L. Pawsey, R.N.. D.J. Doust, M.Sc., and E. Macdonald., Trans. Royal Institution of Naval Architects, London, 1958..

7. "The Effect of Bilge keels on the Rolling of Lightships"-G. Idle and G.S. Baker, Trans. Royal Institution of Naval Architects, 1912, pp.103.

8. "Lightship Cables" -An unpublished Trinity House Report-circa 1933.

9. "Yacht Testing"- J. F. Allan, D.Sc., D. J. Doust, M.Sc., and B. E. Ware, B. Eng., Trans. Royal Institution of Naval Architects, London, U.K. 1957. pp.136

10. "Some Experimental Studies of the Sailing Yacht"- K.S.M. Davidson, Trans. S.N.A.M.E. 1936, pp288.

11. "Some problems of Yacht Measurement"- D. Phillips-Birt., -Trans Royal Institution of Naval Architects, London. U.K., 1958 pp79.

169

12. "Model Experiments on a Series of 0.70 block coefficient forms" R.E. Blackwell, B.Sc. and G.J. Goodrich, B.Sc.- Trans, Royal Institution of Naval Architects, London, U.K., 1957 Part I, pp. 367.

13. "The effect on resistance of variations in breadth-draught ratio, and length-displacement ratio"- R.E. Blackwell, B.Sc. and D.J. Doust, M.Sc., Trans Royal Institution of Naval Architects, London, U.K., 1957, Part II, pp. 407.

14. "The B.S.R.A. Methodical Series- An Overall Presentation"- Variation of resistance with breadth-draught ratio and length-displacement ratio, H. Lackenby, M.Sc. and M.N. Parker, B.Eng., -Trans. Royal Institution of Naval Architects, London, U.K., 1966, pp.363.

15. "The B.S.R.A. Methodical Series- An Overall Presentation", Propulsion Factors, -M.N. Parker, B.Eng., Trans. Royal Institution of Naval Architects, London, U.K., 1966, pp.389

16. "Motions and Propulsion of Single Screw Models in Head Seas -Part II,"- Trans. Royal Institution of Naval Architects, 1970, D.I. Moor, B.Sc. and D.C. Murdey, B.Sc. 1970 pp. 121.

17. "Principles of Naval Architecture"-Written by a Group of Authorities, -Trans. Society of Naval Architects and Marine Engineers, New York, N.Y., 1967.

18. "Statistical Analysis of Resistance data for Trawlers" -Fishing Boats of the World 2, -D.J. Doust, -Fishing News Books Ltd. 1959, pp.370

19. "Resistance and Propulsion of Trawlers"- D.J. Doust & T.P. O'Brien, Trans.-.North East Coast Institution of Engineers & Shipbuilders, Vol.75, 1959 pp.355

20. "Trawler Design at N.P.L."- D.J. Doust, -IV Sesja Naukowa Okretowcow, Szczecin, 1961

21. "A Statistical Analysis of F.A.O. Resistance data for Fishing Craft"- D.J. Doust, J.G. Hayes , T.Tsuchiya- Fishing Boats of the World 3, The Whitefriars Press Ltd. London U.K. 1967

22. "New Possibilities for Improvement in the Design of Fishing Vessels"- J.O. Traung, D.J. Doust, J.G. Hayes.- Fishing Boats of the world 3, ibid. 1967

23. "Optimised Trawler Forms"- D.J. Doust, M.Sc., Trans. North East Coast Institution of Engineers and Shipbuilders., Dec. 1962

List of References

24. "The relative importance of trawler design in the economics of Fishery Operations"- D.J. Doust, -FAO Meeting on Business Decisions in Fishery industries, Report No.22, vol. 2 Rome, 1964

25. "Recent designs of semi-automated fishing vessels"- D.J. Doust, J.Logan, Conference proceedings on Automation and Mechanisation in the Fishing industry, Canadian Fisheries Reports, No.15, July 1970

26. "Fishing Vessel Development"-D.J. Doust, Trans. Society of Naval Architects and Marine Engineers, New York, N.Y. Spring meeting in Honolulu, Hawaii, May 1971.

27. "Expanding the store of statistical and economic information for decision-making in fishery industries"- Robert Hamlisch, F.A.O. Meeting on Business Decisions in Fishery Industries-Rome, September, 1964

28. "Trawler forms with bulbous bows"-D.J. Doust, F.A.O. Conference, Fishing Boats of the World 2, -Fishing News (Books) Ltd. pp. 445

29. "A method of determining the flow pattern around the stern of ship models" D.J. Doust and V.A. Daniels, Conference on the Analysis of Research Film, N.P.L. Report 30-31 May 1961

30. "Calculation of Horse Power for Marine Propulsion" by Lt. Col. Thomas English, Proceedings of the Institution of Mechanical Engineers" January, 1896.

31. "An analysis of the profitability of a fishing fleet"- by D.J. Doust and J.G. Hayes, -N.P.L. unpublished report, circa.1965

32. "New Ship Hydrodynamics Laboratory"-by J.F. Allan, D.Sc. Trans. Royal Institution of Naval Architects, London, U.K.-1957 pp. 326

33. "The Expert Witness"- by David J. Doust, published by Pachelle Inc. P.O.Box 381, Ayer's Cliff, Quebec, JOB1CO Canadian cataloging, ISBN 0-9681858-0-0

34. Supreme Court of Canada Judgement #25340 dated December 18, 1997

35. "Annual report of the Inter-American Tuna Commission-1978", La Jolla, California, U.S.A.

36. "Modern Fishing Gear of the World"-(3), F.A.O. published by Fishing News (Books) Ltd. pp. 395 and edited by Hilmar Kristjonsson.

37. "Marine Design Manual, for Fiberglass Reinforced Plastics" -Gibbs & Cox Inc. N.Y. 1960- McGraw-Hill Book Company, Inc.

38. An evaluation of F.R.P. fishing vessesl in the United States. -Confidential Report by CDD Marine Inc.

39. The magazine "Navy" , November 1971

40. "Strength of Aluminum"- Alcan Canada Products Limited, 4th. edition, April,1973

41. "Hydrodynamics in Ship Design"- vol 2, by Harold E. Saunders, published by SNAME 1957, pp.629

42. "The Settlement of Marine Disputes" Paper #16, -Marine Experts and the Legal Process, by D. J. Doust, published by The Royal Institution of Naval Architects, London, 1998

43. Lord Woolf's Report- see web site <http://www.open.gov.uk/lcd/justice>

44. TRANSATLANTIC v HERMES- The Exchequer Court of Canada, Judgement #B-814, Ottawa, Sept 10, 1968

45. "Conditions of Contract-The Rules of the Game" by A.J. Rogan, Conference on "Newbuild 2000 and the Role of the Naval Architect in Ship and Offshore Projects", -Royal Society of Arts, London, 24-25 October, 1995

46. Federal Court of Canada, Judgement #T-7690-82, dated May 6, 1987, KRUGER v BALTIC SHIPPING COMPANY- re. sinking of M.V. "Mekhanik Tarasov".

47. Ship Design and Construction, written by a group of authorities, SNAME, New York, N.Y. 1980

48. "Warship Technology"-August 1998. Supplement to "The Naval Architect", International Journal of the Royal Institution of Naval Architects. London, U.K.

49. Journal -"Ship and Boat International" -June, 1998

50. Lloyds Register-"Rules and Regulations for the Classification of Ships"- Part 6, 1997

51. Bureau Veritas- Rules for Ships, Part III-Chapter 19, 1997

52. Det Norske Veritas Classification AS- Part 4, Chapter 5,1997

List of References

53. Journal-"Ship and Boat International"-September, 1998

54. MacGregor News, Issue 135-Autumn 1998

55. "The optimum hull form parameters" by J. G. Hayes. - Proceedings of a conference " Numerical Methods Applied to Shipbuilding"-Oslo-Bergen, 1963.- A Nato Advanced Study Institute, organised by and proceedings published by the Central Institute for Industrial Research and Det Norske Veritas, 1964.

CHAPTER XIII

LIST OF FIGURES

CHAPTER XIV

NOMENCLATURE

"A" frames	Metal frames in the shape of the letter "A", from which pulleys and other attachments can be suspended.
A.C.	Alternating current, which is in the form of a sine wave.
A.N.S.I.	American National Standards Institute.
A.W.S.	American Welding Standards.
Acceleration	Rate of change of velocity of a moving object, in a specific direction.
Acoustic mines	Explosive mines dropped on the sea bed, which were activated by pressure changes as ships as passed over them.
Advance coefficient	The speed of advance of a propeller, divided by the product of its diameter and the number of revolutions.
Anemometer	An instrument for measuring wind speed and direction.
Angle of run	The angle from the ships centreline made by a tangent to the outer shape of a ship, when it is cut by a horizontal plane at any waterline.
Annealing	A heating process followed by slow cooling, which relieves stresses locked-up in a metal.
Argon	An inert gaseous element.
Armature	An open- meshed mould, used as the basic skeleton, from which the shape of the vessel can be constructed.
Aspect Ratio	The square of the span of a wing or rudder, divided by its area.
B.S.R.A.	British Ship Research Association.
Balsa	A light- weight American wood.
Basic	Describes a method of steel making which uses alkaline materials.
Bernoulli's Theorem	A theorem which relates the pressure, velocity and depth of a stream of water to its energy per unit mass.
Berthing	Bringing a ship alongside a quay or jetty, or into a dock.

177

Best evidence	Evidence which appears to the court to be the most credible, in the light of all the other evidence. (Doust)
Bilge keels	Plates which project normal to the hull, and which are usually fitted at the turn of bilge.
Bilges	The portion of a ship where the sides meet the bottom, and sometimes called the "turn of bilge".
Bobbins	Metal spheres attached to the bottom edges of a fishing net, which enable it to stay close to the sea bottom.
Body plan	A ship plan, which consists of a series of transverse intersections with the outer shape of the ship, made by vertical planes at right angles to its centre-line plane.
Bonjean curves	Curves which depict the transverse sectional areas of a ship at specific heights above the keel, at various sections along the ship. (Bonjean)
Boom and tackle	An overhead boom, from which is suspended a continuous, chain-driven, lifting tackle.
Boundary layer	The fluid adjacent to the hull surface of a moving ship, within which most of the frictional forces are concentrated.
Bread and butter	A system of construction for wooden models, in which layers of wood are glued together and shaped to give the correct hull form.
Bulbous bow	The bulb-shaped underwater bow of a ship, which projects below the waterline.
Buttock slope	The angle from the horizontal made by a tangent to the outer shape of a ship, when it is cut by a vertical plane parallel to its centreline.
C.I.B.C.	Canadian Imperial Bank of Commerce.
C.R.O	A cathode ray oscilloscope, similar to a television screen.
Canal	Also known as a channel, in which ships are able to navigate on inland waterways.
Cartesian system	A rectangular system of co-ordinates, which defines a point in space by its distance from three axes at right angles, x, y and z.
Cavitate	Breakdown of flow which occurs when the pressure at the surface of a rotating propeller blade, falls below its local vapour pressure.
Centre board	The keel of a yacht which is often designed to be retractable.

Nomenclature

Centre of buoyancy The point within a ship, or floating object, at which the the whole of the upward buoyancy force may be assumed to act.

Centre of Effort The point within an area such as a sail, or a keel, at which wind or water forces are asumed to act.

Classification Society An authority which classifies ships and other marine structures to certain acceptable standards of construction.

Close hauled When a yacht is sailing against the wind.

Coamings Raised, circular watertight covers, usually 24 inches in height on the weather deck, leading down into the ship.

Coasters Cargo ships which work around coastal ports.

Composite ships Ships made of wood and sheathed in copper.

Compression blocks Blocks of hardened metal, through which steel wire ropes are pulled and squashed, to provide a restraining force. (Hiley)

Container ship A ship specially designed for the carriage of containers, below and above the upper deck.

Containers Mainly having dimensions 40 feet long by 8.0 feet wide and 8.0 feet deep, and sealed for ocean, road and rail cargo transportion, by door to door delivery. They can be of steel or aluminum construction.

Croaker A popular name for certain sea and fresh water fish which croak when caught.

Cryogenic Capable of being frozen.

D.C. Direct current, which stays at a constant level.

D.W.T. Dead Weight Tons, as a measure of ship carrying capacity. (D.W.T. ton =2,240 pounds)

Deep- sea Ocean depth.

Diesel- Electric Diesel machinery driving electrical motors, which power the ship's propellers.

Double bilge keels Plates which project normal to the hull surface, fitted above and below the turn of bilge.

Double bottom The structure at the bottom of a ship, between the outer bottom plating and the inner bottom plating which runs closely above it, and which combine to form the double bottom.

Dynamometer An instrument for measuring forces.

Elastic limit The range within which stress in a metal is directly proportional to the strain.

The Naval Architect

Electric furnace	A furnace for making steel using electrical current to heat the metal.
Engine torque	The twisting moment which turns an engine.
Epoxy resins	Syrup-like laminates, adhesives or coatings which can be cured into hard solids by the addition of a curing agent.
F.A.O	Food and Agriculture Organisation of the United Nations.
Fitted out	The stage during the building of a ship when all the internal machinery, equipment and furnishings are installed.
Freeboard	The vertical height of the top of the deck at the side of a ship, measured above the floating waterline.
Freeing ports	Side openings in the ship's sides which permit water to drain off the deck.
Grain boards	Boards which are fitted in cargo holds of ships carrying grain, to restrict the movement of the grain due to the ship motion.
Grounding	This occurs when a ship touches the bottom of a channel, river or the sea bed.
Gyroscope	A weighted disc, rotating at high speed in bearings, which maintains its position in space, and used as a reference plane from which to measure angular changes, such as roll, pitch and yaw.
Hake	"Merlucius vulgaris"-a sea fish allied to the cod.
Hatch covers	Fabricated construction which covers the hatches of a cargo ship, and which are often reinforced for the stowage of additional deck cargo, such as containers.
Hawse pipe	The housing in which anchor cable is contained, where it enters the ship.
Heel	The angle of inclination of a ship from the vertical plane through its centreline.
Heel	The bottom part of a rudder.
Helium	An inert non-inflammable gas.
Hopper dredgers	Vessels which dredge the sea bed and carry away the dredged material on board.
Hove -to	When a ship holds its position at sea, under stormy conditions, without proceeding to its destination.
Hydrodynmics	A branch of dynamics which calculates the forces and motions of fluids around bodies, such as ships, in which case the fluid is usually water.

Nomenclature

Inclining tests   Experiments made on a ship to determine to its stability when heeled, by moving known weights across the deck and recording the angles of heel.

Inner bottom   The deck plating of a ship fitted immediately above the double bottom.

Isotropic materials   Materials which have the same physical properties in all directions.

Kamaboko   A Japanese-processed fish, used as the basis of other food.

Kevlar   A patented composite building material.

Laker vessel   A cargo ship which is specially designed to work on the Great Lakes and in the St. Lawrence Seaway system.

Lamellar separation   This occurs within a metal when external forces pull it apart.

Lashings   Steel wire ropes or rods, used to secure containers on board ships.

Lateral wind centre   The point where all of the wind forces on the ship's side may be assumed to act.

Least squares   A statistical measure which minimises the sum of squares of differences of a series of measurements, from their average value.

Light Vessel   An anchored vessel, fitted with special light and sound emission systems, to warn other ships of hazards to navigation in the immediate vicinity.

Lightship   The weight of a ship without its crew, passengers, fuel, water ballast, cargo or stores.

Lines plan   A drawing of the outer shape of a ship, from which it can be constructed.

List   The steady inclination of a ship to one side or the other.

Marlin spike   A conical hand tool, used to open up the strands of a rope, when splicing it.

Mat   Fibreglass composed of strands of filaments, woven together in mat form.

Metallurgist   One who is qualified in the practice of extracting metal from the ore, and who can assess its composition and physical properties.

Midship section   The section of a ship made by a transverse plane cutting through its mid length.

Mizzen sail   The sail for the after mast of a sailing ship, nearest to the stern.

181

Molotov cocktail	An explosive incendiary device used in the second World War.
MPa	Mega-Pascals, a measure of pressure in the "Système International d'Unites", known as the SI system.
N.P.L.	National Physical Laboratory- the leading Government research institution in the U.K.
N.P.V.	Net Present Value, which refers all anticipated cash flows for a project back to their current value.
Newton's Laws	Physical laws which all moving bodies must obey, and to which they are subjected.
Open hearth	A method of steel making which uses pre-heated gas and air to melt the metal.
Outer bottom	The external structure of a ship which is at the bottom, from the keel to the turn of the bilge.
Pelagic species	Fish species which usually live at mid-ocean depth, and which tend to travel in groups, such as herring and tuna.
Period of encounter	The time between two successive waves, arriving at any point on a ship.
Piles	Reinforced-concrete structure used to support the foundations of buildings.
Pilot brig	A two-masted vessel moored at anchor, and used to house river pilots.
Pintle	The shaft about which the rudder turns, and to which it is attached.
Pitch	The repetitive oscillating motion of ship in the vertical plane, bow up and bow down.
Pitot tubes	Thin tubes which measure the flow velocity or pressure at a point in a fluid.
Pollock	"Gadius pollachius"- a sea fish allied to the whiting.
Pozzolan	The popular name for "Pozzuolana"-A volcanic ash used as an ingredient of cement or mortar.
Purse- seining	A system of fishing with a large, purse-shaped net, used by fishing vessels to encircle fish, such as tuna or herring and similar species.
PVC	Poly Vinyl Chloride.
R.I.N.A.	Royal Institution of Naval Architects, London, England.
Regression analysis	Estimating underlying relationships between dependent and independent variables, using statistical methods.
Regression equation	An equation derived from a statistical analysis.
Ring dolphin	A floating device used to assist the berthing of ships.

Nomenclature

Riveting	A method of ship construction by which metal plates are joined together by heated rivets, inserted in matching holes in the plates and hammered close together from either side.
Roll	The repetitive oscillating motion of a ship to one side and then the other.
Root stresses	The stresses which occur at the intersection of a propeller blade with the boss, to which it is attached.
Rovings	Fibreglass filaments which can be woven into coarse fabric and used in boat construction.
Salvage	The recovery of a ship which is either sunk, grounded or abandoned.
Scale effects	Any differences between full scale results measured on a ship, and those measured on its corresponding model.
Self-trimming	Holds designed so that the cargo will automatically fill the holds without other handling, as loading takes place.
Self-unloaders	Cargo ships fitted with their own internal cargo unloading system, consisting of conveyor belts and transporter booms to discharge to shore, or to other ships.
SES	Surface Effect Ships.
Side trawler	A fishing vessel which drags a fishing net over the side - usually the starboard side.
Sideways launching	The launching of a ship at right angles to its length, usually into a river or water of restricted width.
Silver Cod Trophy	A trophy which was awarded each year to the top earner in the British fishing fleet.
Span	The breadth of a wing or rudder in the line of fluid flow.
Speed made good	The speed which a yacht makes against the wind.
Static drop	The vertical drop of a side-launched ship as it moves down the launching ways.
Stern gallows	Steel frames which carry the trawl warps, and boards, usually one each side at the stern.
Stern post	The supporting structure for the rudder at the stern of a ship.
Stern ramp	An inclined, sloping surface at the stern of a fishing vessel, up which the netted fish are dragged on board.
Stern trawler	A fishing vessel which pulls its net over the stern and sometimes referred to as a "dragger."
Stern tube	A cylindrical tube in which a propeller shaft rotates on its bearings.

Strain	The elongation of a metal under stress divided by its length.
Stud link	Oval shaped link fitted with a cross stud at the middle of its length.
Surimi	A Japanese-processed fish, used as the basis other foods.
T'ween deck	Usually the deck immediately below the upper deck of a cargo ship.
Tank tests	Tests of ship performance conducted in a large tank filled with water, in which ship models are towed or propelled, and their efficiency measured.
Tank top	The structure at the top of a ship's double bottom, which thus forms the bottom part of the ship's hold.
"Tayco" steel	A special type of steel used to make anchor chain and cable.
Techno-economics	Technical and economic data used to deduce optimum overall conditions of performance.
Thickness ratio	The maximum thickness of a propeller or rudder section, divided by its length.
Toughness	The quality of a metal to be flexible, without being brittle.
Trawl boards	Wooden boards, which act like a kite under water when towed from a fishing vessel, and attached to the mouth of the net to keep it open.
Trawl warps	The steel ropes which pull the fishing nets.
Trial results	Results usually obtained by running a ship over a measured mile, at a series of speeds, to check its performance.
Tug and barge	Barges under tow by a tug, either pulling ahead or pushing from the stern.
Under-deck	Usually refers to the space of a ship below the upper deck.
Velocity	Rate of change of distance of a moving object in a specific direction, otherwise it is known as the speed.
Ways	Wooden structure on which a vessel sits as it slides down to enter the water.
Welding	The joining together of metal structure by fusion.
Wood floors	The vertical parts of a wooden boat immediately above the outer bottom, which strengthen the bottom and extend from bilge to bilge.

Nomenclature

Yaw	The turning motion of a ship to either port or starboard, that is bow to the left or bow to the right.
Yield strength	The tensile stress at which a large increase in elongation occurs, just beyond the elastic limit.